TI-84 Plus
TI-84 Plus Silver Edition
Guidebook

22 23 24 25

Important Information

Texas Instruments makes no warranty, either express or implied, including but not limited to any implied warranties of merchantability and fitness for a particular purpose, regarding any programs or book materials and makes such materials available solely on an "as-is" basis. In no event shall Texas Instruments be liable to anyone for special, collateral, incidental, or consequential damages in connection with or arising out of the purchase or use of these materials, and the sole and exclusive liability of Texas Instruments, regardless of the form of action, shall not exceed the purchase price of this product. Moreover, Texas Instruments shall not be liable for any claim of any kind whatsoever against the use of these materials by any other party.

USA FCC Information Concerning Radio Frequency Interference

This equipment has been tested and found to comply with the limits for a Class B digital device, pursuant to Part 15 of the FCC rules. These limits are designed to provide reasonable protection against harmful interference in a residential installation. This equipment generates, uses, and can radiate radio frequency energy and, if not installed and used in accordance with the instructions, may cause harmful interference to radio communications. However, there is no guarantee that interference will not occur in a particular installation.

If this equipment does cause harmful interference to radio or television reception, which can be determined by turning the equipment off and on, you can try to correct the interference by one or more of the following measures:

* Reorient or relocate the receiving antenna.

* Increase the separation between the equipment and receiver.

* Connect the equipment into an outlet on a circuit different from that to which the receiver is connected.

* Consult the dealer or an experienced radio/television technician for help.

Caution: Any changes or modifications to this equipment not expressly approved by Texas Instruments may void your authority to operate the equipment.

About the TI-84 Plus and TI-84 Plus Silver Edition

The TI-84 Plus Silver Edition is the same as the TI-84 Plus except:

- it has more memory, and thus more spaces for graphing calculator software applications (Apps).

- it has interchangeable faceplates that let you customize the appearance of your TI-84 Plus Silver Edition.

Since all the functions of the TI-84 Plus Silver Edition and the TI-84 Plus are the same, this guidebook can be used for either the TI-84 Plus or the TI-84 Plus Silver Edition.

The CD included with your TI-84 Plus / TI-84 Plus Silver Edition package also includes an electronic guidebook, which is a complete reference manual for the TI-84 Plus / TI-84 Plus Silver Edition. If the CD is not available, you can download a copy of the electronic guidebook from the Texas Instruments web page at:

education.ti.com/guides

The TI-84 Plus / TI-84 Plus Silver Edition has some graphing calculator software applications (Apps) preinstalled. For information about these Apps, see the electronic documentation files on the Texas Instrument web page at:

education.ti.com/guides

About this book

This guidebook gives a quick overview of each topic, along with keystroke instructions for easy examples. All examples assume that the TI-84 Plus is using default settings. For complete information on any topic, see the electronic guidebook on the CD that came with your graphing calculator.

Contents

Getting Started

TI-84 Plus keys

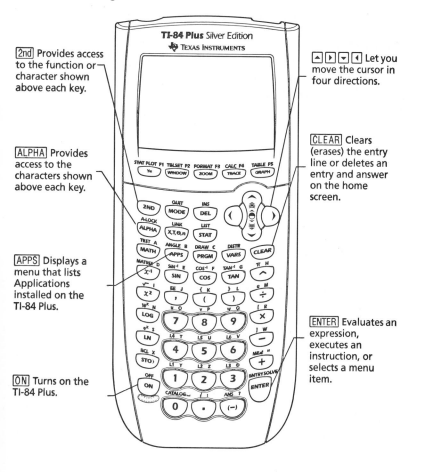

2nd Provides access to the function or character shown above each key.

ALPHA Provides access to the characters shown above each key.

APPS Displays a menu that lists Applications installed on the TI-84 Plus.

ON Turns on the TI-84 Plus.

▲ ▶ ▼ ◀ Let you move the cursor in four directions.

CLEAR Clears (erases) the entry line or deletes an entry and answer on the home screen.

ENTER Evaluates an expression, executes an instruction, or selects a menu item.

Turning the TI-84 Plus on and off

To turn on the TI-84 Plus, press ⟨ON⟩. The ⟨ON⟩ key is located at the lower left corner of the TI-84 Plus.

To turn off the TI-84 Plus, press the ⟨2nd⟩ key followed by the ⟨ON⟩ key. OFF is the *second* function of ⟨ON⟩.

When you turn off the TI-84 Plus, all settings and memory contents are retained. The next time you turn on the TI-84 Plus, the home screen displays as it was when you last used it.

Automatic Power Down™

To prolong the life of the batteries, Automatic Power Down™ (APD™) turns off the TI-84 Plus automatically after about five minutes without any activity. The next time you turn on the TI-84 Plus, it is exactly as you left it.

Home screen

When you turn on your TI-84 Plus the first time, you should see this screen:

TI-84 Plus Silver Edition
2.30

RAM cleared

To clear this text from your screen, press [CLEAR] twice. You should now see the home screen, a blank screen with a flashing cursor. The home screen is where you enter problems and see results.

If you pressed [CLEAR] above and you still do not see a blank home screen, press the [2nd] key followed by the [MODE] key (to select QUIT).

Example: Add 2 + 3 on the home screen.

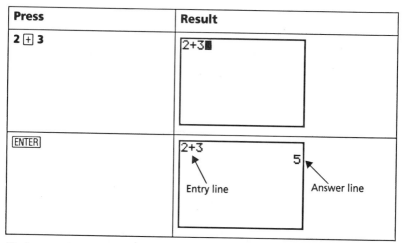

Press	Result
2 [+] 3	2+3■
[ENTER]	2+3 Entry line 5 Answer line

Note: Results are displayed on the next line (the answer line), not on the entry line.

Example: Multiply 5 x 4.

Press	Result
5 ⊠ 4 ENTER	5*4 20

2nd *and* ALPHA *keys*

Most keys on the TI-84 Plus can perform two or more functions. To use a function printed on a key, press the key. To use a function printed above a key, you must first press the 2nd key or the ALPHA key.

2nd key

Second functions are printed above the keys (the same color as the 2nd key). Some secondary functions enter a function or a symbol on the home screen (sin^{-1} or $\sqrt{\ }$, for example). Others display menus or editors.

To view the ANGLE menu, for example, look for ANGLE above the APPS key near the top of the TI-84 Plus keyboard. Press the 2nd key (and then release it) and then press APPS. In this guidebook the key combination is indicated by 2nd [ANGLE], not 2nd APPS.

Note: The flashing cursor changes to ▯ when you press the 2nd key.

ALPHA key

The ALPHA key lets you enter the alphabetic characters and some special symbols. To enter T, for example, press ALPHA (and then release it) and then press 4. In the guidebook this key combination is indicated by ALPHA [T].

If you have several alphabetic characters to enter, press 2nd [A-LOCK] to avoid having to press the ALPHA key multiple times. This locks the alpha key in the *On* position until you press ALPHA a second time to unlock it.

Note: The flashing cursor changes to ▯ when you press the ALPHA key.

CLEAR *and* [2nd] [QUIT]

CLEAR key

The CLEAR key erases the home screen. This key is located just below the four arrow keys at the upper right corner of the TI-84 Plus keyboard. If you press CLEAR during an entry, it clears the entry line. If you press CLEAR when the cursor is on a blank line, it clears everything on the home screen.

Although it does not affect the calculation, it is frequently helpful to clear the previous work from the home screen before you begin a new problem. As you work through this guide, we recommend that you press CLEAR each time you begin a new *Example*. This removes the previous example from the home screen and ensures that the screen you see matches the one shown in the example.

[2nd] [QUIT]

If you accidentally press a menu key, pressing CLEAR will usually return you to the home screen, but in most cases pressing [2nd] [QUIT] to leave the menu and return to the home screen.

Entering an expression

An expression consists of numbers, variables, operators, functions, and their arguments that evaluate to a single answer. 2X + 2 is an expression.

Type the expression, and then press [ENTER] to evaluate it. To enter a function or instruction on the entry line, you can:

*   Press its key, if available. For example, press [LOG].

    — or —

*   Select it from the CATALOG, if the function appears on the CATALOG. For example, press [2nd] [CATALOG], press ▾ to move down to **log(**, and press [ENTER] to select **log(**.

    — or —

*   Select it from a menu, if available. For example, to find the **round** function, press [MATH], press ▸ to select **NUM**, then select **2:round(**.

Example: Enter and evaluate the expression π × 2.

Press	Result
[2nd] [π] [×] **2**	π*2
[ENTER]	π*2 6.283185307

Interchangeable Faceplates

The TI-84 Plus Silver Edition has interchangeable faceplates that let you customize the appearance of your unit. To purchase additional faceplates, refer to the TI Online Store at **education.ti.com**.

Removing a Faceplate

1. Lift the tab at the bottom edge of the faceplate away from the TI-84 Plus Silver Edition case.

2. Carefully lift the faceplate away from the unit until it releases. Be careful not to damage the faceplate or the keyboard.

Installing New Faceplates

1. Align the top of the faceplate in the corresponding grooves of the TI-84 Plus Silver Edition case.

2. Gently click the faceplate into place. Do not force.

3. Make sure you gently press each of the grooves to ensure the faceplate is installed properly. See the diagram for proper groove placement.

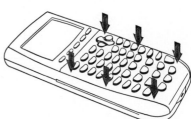

Using the Clock

Use the Clock to set the time and date, select the clock display format, and turn the clock on and off. The clock is turned on by default and is accessed from the mode screen.

Displaying the Clock Settings

1. Press [MODE]

2. Press the ⊡ to move the cursor to **SET CLOCK**.

3. Press [ENTER].

Changing the Clock settings

1. Press the ⊡ or ⊡ to highlight the date format you want, example: M/D/Y. Press [ENTER].

2. Press ⊡ to highlight YEAR. Press [CLEAR] and type the year, example: 2004.

3. Press ⊡ to highlight MONTH. Press [CLEAR] and type the number of the month (a number from 1–12).

4. Press ⊡ to highlight DAY. Press [CLEAR] and type the date.

5. Press ⊡ to highlight TIME. Press ⊡ or ⊡ to highlight the time format you want. Press [ENTER].

6. Press ⊡ to highlight HOUR. Press [CLEAR] and type the hour. A number from 1–12 or 0–23.

7. Press ⊡ to highlight MINUTE. Press [CLEAR] and type the minutes. A number from 0–59.

8. Press ⊡ to highlight AM/PM. Press ⊡ or ⊡ to highlight the format. Press [ENTER].

9. To Save changes, press ⊡ to select **SAVE**. Press [ENTER].

Error Messages

If you type the wrong date for the month, for example: June 31, June does not have 31 days, you will receive an error message with two choices:

```
ERR:DATE
1:Quit
2:Goto

Invalid day for
month selected.
```

- To Quit the Clock application and return to the Home screen, select 1: Quit. Press ENTER.

   — or —

- To return to the clock application and correct the error, select 2: Goto. Press ENTER.

Turning the Clock On

There are two options to turn the clock on. One option is through the MODE screen, the other is through the Catalog.

Using the Mode Screen to turn the clock on

1. If the Clock is turned off, Press ⊡ to highlight **TURN CLOCK ON**.

2. Press [ENTER].

Using the Catalog to turn the clock on

1. If the Clock is turned off, Press [2nd] [CATALOG]

2. Press ⊡ or ⊡ to scroll the CATALOG until the selection cursor points to **ClockOn**.

3. Press [ENTER] [ENTER].

Turning the Clock Off

1. Press [2nd] [CATALOG].

2. Press ⊡ or ⊡ to scroll the CATALOG until the selection cursor points to **ClockOff**.

3. Press [ENTER] [ENTER].

ClockOff will turn off the Clock display.

TI-84 Plus menus

Many functions and instructions are entered on the home screen by selecting from a menu.

To select an item from the displayed menu:

* Press the number or letter shown at the left of that item.

  — or —

* Use the cursor arrow keys, ⬇ or ⬆, to highlight the item, and then press [ENTER].

Some menus close automatically when you make a selection, but if the menu remains open, press [2nd] [QUIT] to exit. Do not press [CLEAR] to exit, since this will sometimes delete your selection.

Example: Enter $\sqrt[3]{27}$ on the home screen entry line.

Press	Result	
[MATH]	**MATH** NUM CPX PRB 1▶Frac 2:▶Dec 3:³ 4:³√(5:ˣ√ 6:fMin(7↓fMax(	Menus containing an arrow next to the final item continue on a second page.
4 — or — ⬇ ⬇ ⬇ [ENTER]	³√(▮	
27 [)] [ENTER]	³√(27) 3	

Example: Change the FORMAT menu setting to display grid points on the graph.

Press	Result
[2nd] [FORMAT]	RectGC PolarGC CoordOn CoordOff GridOff GridOn AxesOn AxesOff LabelOff LabelOn ExprOn ExprOff
▼ ▼ ▶ [ENTER]	RectGC PolarGC CoordOn CoordOff GridOff GridOn AxesOn AxesOff LabelOff LabelOn ExprOn ExprOff
[GRAPH]	

Example: Turn off the display of grid points.

Press	Result
[2nd] [FORMAT] ▼ ▼ [ENTER]	RectGC PolarGC CoordOn CoordOff GridOff GridOn AxesOn AxesOff LabelOff LabelOn ExprOn ExprOff

Note: Press [2nd] [QUIT] or [CLEAR] to close the FORMAT menu and return to the home screen.

Summary of menus on the TI-84 Plus

Press	To display
[APPS]	**APPLICATIONS** menu — to see a list of TI-84 Plus graphing calculator software applications (APPS).

Press	To display
[2nd] [LINK]	**LINK** menu — to communicate with another graphing calculator.
[2nd] [MEM]	**MEMORY** menu — to check available memory and manage existing memory.
[MATH]	**MATH** menu — to select a math operation.
[VARS]	**VARS** menu — to select variable names to paste to the home screen.
[2nd] [STAT PLOT]	**STAT PLOTS** menu — to define statistical plots.
[2nd] [CATALOG]	**CATALOG** menu — to select from a complete, alphabetic list of all TI-84 Plus built-in functions and instructions.
[2nd] [FORMAT]	**FORMAT** menu — to define a graph's appearance.
[2nd] [MATRIX]	**MATRIX** menu — to define, view, and edit matrices.
[2nd] [DRAW]	**DRAW** menu — to select tools for drawing on graphs.
[2nd] [DISTR]	**DISTRIBUTIONS** menu — to select distribution functions to paste to the home screen or editor screens.
[2nd] [TEST]	**TEST** menu — to select relational operators (=, ≠, ≤, ≥, etc.) and Boolean operators (and, or, xor, not) to paste to the home screen.

Editing and deleting

You can change any expression or entry using the backspace ◁ key, the delete DEL key, or the insert 2nd [INS] key.

Example: Enter the expression $5^2 + 1$, and then change the expression to $5^2 + 5$.

Press	Result
5 x^2 + **1**	5^2+1■
◁ **5**	5^2+5

Example: Enter the expression $5^2 + 1$, and then change the expression to $5^2 - 5$.

Press	Result
5 x^2 + **1**	5^2+1■
◁ ◁ DEL DEL	5^2

Press	Result
☐ 5 ENTER	5^2-5 20

Example: Change the example above to 5^2 + 2 − 5 using 2nd [ENTRY] to recall the expression and 2nd [INS] to insert + 2 into the expression.

Press	Result
2nd [ENTRY]	5^2-5■
◄ ◄ 2nd [INS] ⊞ 2 ENTER	5^2+2-5 22

Using ⊟ *and* ⊡

Many graphing calculators (including the TI-84 Plus) make a distinction between the symbols for subtraction and negation.

Use ⊟ to enter subtraction operations. Use ⊡ to enter a negative number in an operation, in an expression, or on a setup screen.

Example: Subtract 10 from 25.

Press	Result
2 5 ⊟ 1 0 [ENTER]	25-10 　　　　　　15

Example: Add 10 to ⁻25.

Press	Result
⊡ 2 5 ⊞ 1 0 [ENTER]	⁻25+10 　　　　　⁻15

Example: Subtract ⁻10 from 25.

Press	Result
2 5 ⊟ ⊡ 1 0 [ENTER]	25--10 　　　　　35

Note: Notice that the TI-84 Plus displays a slightly different symbol for negation and subtraction to make it easier for you to distinguish between the two. The negative symbol is raised and slightly shorter.

Using parentheses

Since all calculations inside parentheses are completed first, it is sometimes important to place a portion of an expression inside parentheses.

Example: Multiply 4∗1+2; then multiply 4∗(1+2).

Press	Result
4 ⊠ 1 ⊞ 2 [ENTER]	4∗1+2 6

4 ⊠ ⟮ 1 ⊞ 2 ⟯
[ENTER]
	4∗1+2
	        6
	4∗(1+2)
	       12

Note: The closing parenthesis ⟯ is optional. The operation will be completed if you omit it. The exception to this rule occurs when there is another operation following the parenthetical operation. In this case, you must include the closing parenthesis.

Example: Divide 1/2 by 2/3.

Press	Result
⟮ 1 ⟌ 2 ⟯ ⟌ ⟮ 2 ⟌ 3 ⟯ [ENTER]	(1/2)/(2/3) .75

Example: Calculate $16 ^ \wedge \frac{1}{2}$.

Press	Result
1 6 [^] [(] **1** [÷] **2** [)] [ENTER]	16^(1/2) 4

Example: Calculate $(-3)^2$.

Press	Result
[(] [(-)] **3** [)] [x^2] [ENTER]	(-3)² 9

Note: Try each of these examples without the parentheses and see what happens!

Storing a value

Values are stored to and recalled from memory using variable names.

Example: Store 25 to variable A and multiply A by 2.

Press	Result
2 5 STO► ALPHA [A]	25→A
ENTER	25→A 25
2 × ALPHA [A] ENTER	25→A 25 2*A 50
— or — ALPHA [A] × **2** ENTER	25→A 25 2*A 50 A*2 50

Example: Find the value of $2X^3 - 5X^2 - 7X + 10$ when $X = {}^-0.5$.

Press	Result
(-) . **5** STO► X,T,Θ,*n* ENTER (stores -.5 to X)	-.5→X -.5

Press	Result

2 $\boxed{\text{X,T,}\Theta,n}$ $\boxed{\wedge}$ 3
 $\boxed{-}$ 5 $\boxed{\text{X,T,}\Theta,n}$ $\boxed{x^2}$
 $\boxed{-}$ 7 $\boxed{\text{X,T,}\Theta,n}$ $\boxed{+}$ 1 0
 $\boxed{\text{ENTER}}$
	``
	-.5→X
	              -.5
	2X^3-5X²-7X+10
	               12
	``

You can remove a value stored to a variable using the DELVAR function or by storing 0 to the variable.

Example: Delete the value (-.5) stored to X above by storing 0.

Press	Result
0 $\boxed{\text{STO►}}$ $\boxed{\text{X,T,}\Theta,n}$ $\boxed{\text{ENTER}}$	``` 0→X 0 ```

$\boxed{\text{X,T,}\Theta,n}$
 $\boxed{\text{ENTER}}$
	``
	0→X
	                0
	X
	                0
	``

Graphing a function

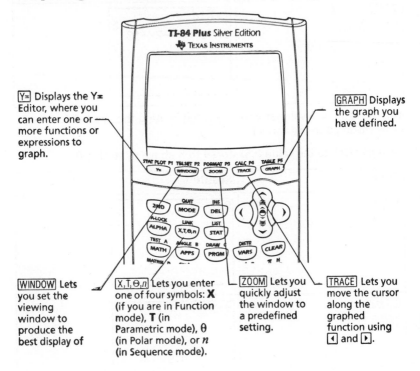

Y= Displays the Y= Editor, where you can enter one or more functions or expressions to graph.

GRAPH Displays the graph you have defined.

WINDOW Lets you set the viewing window to produce the best display of

X,T,Θ,n Lets you enter one of four symbols: **X** (if you are in Function mode), **T** (in Parametric mode), θ (in Polar mode), or *n* (in Sequence mode).

ZOOM Lets you quickly adjust the window to a predefined setting.

TRACE Lets you move the cursor along the graphed function using ◄ and ►.

To graph a function, you must:

1. Display the Y= Editor.
2. Enter the function.
3. Display the graph.

Note: If you previously changed graph type in the mode settings, you must change the type back to Func (the default setting) before you graph.

Example: Graph the function Y = X² + 1.

Press	Result
Y=	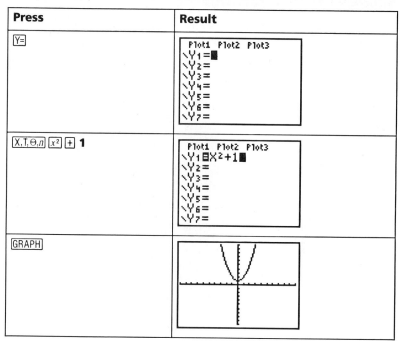
X,T,Θ,n x² + 1	
GRAPH	

Note: If Y1 is not empty, press CLEAR. If there are additional entries in the Y= Editor, press ⯆ CLEAR until all are clear.

Changing mode settings

The mode settings determine how entries are interpreted and how answers are displayed on the TI-84 Plus.

Example: Change the mode setting for decimals from *Float* to *3* decimal places.

Press	Result
[MODE]	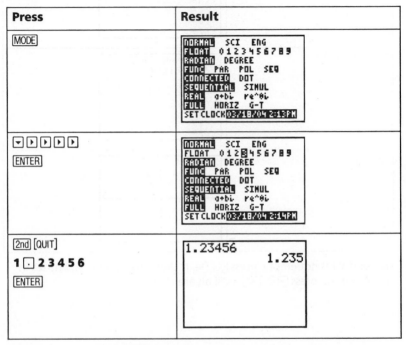
⊡ ▷ ▷ ▷ ▷ [ENTER]	
[2nd] [QUIT] 1 ⊡ 2 3 4 5 6 [ENTER]	1.23456 　　　　1.235

Note: You must press [ENTER] to change a mode setting. If you highlight the setting and then exit the mode menu without pressing [ENTER], the setting will not be changed.

The mode menu includes the following settings (*denotes the default setting in each row):

Setting	Choices
Numeric notation	• *Normal:* for example, 12345.67 • *Sci* (scientific): for example, 1.234567E4 • *Eng* (engineering): for example, 12.34567E3

Setting	Choices
Decimal	• *Float: lets the number of decimal places change based on the result (up to 10 digits) • 0–9: sets the number of decimal places to a value (0–9) that you specify
Angle measure	• *Radian: interprets angle values as radians • Degree: interprets angle values as degrees
Type of graph	• *Func (functional): plots functions, where Y is a function of X • Par (parametric): plots relations, where X and Y are functions of T • Pol (polar): plots functions, where r is a function of [n] θ • Seq (sequence): plots sequences, where the nth term of u, v, or w is defined recursively or explicitly.
Plot type	• *Connected: draws a line connecting each point calculated for the selected functions • Dot: plots only the calculated points of the selected functions
Sequential or simultaneous graphing	• *Sequential: draws graphs one at a time • Simul (simultaneous): draws several graphs at the same time
Real or complex mode	• *Real: displays real numbers, such as 1, 1/2, $\sqrt{3}$ • a+bi (rectangular complex): displays as 3+2i • re^θi (polar complex): displays as re^θi
Screen display	• *Full: displays full screen • Horiz: displays a horizontal split screen • G-T: displays a vertical split screen (graph & table)

The importance of mode settings

Example: Multiply 2/3 × 2.

Press	Result
[MODE] [▼] [▶] [ENTER]	**NORMAL** SCI ENG **FLOAT** **0**123456789 **RADIAN** DEGREE **FUNC** PAR POL SEQ **CONNECTED** DOT **SEQUENTIAL** SIMUL **REAL** a+bi re^θi **FULL** HORIZ G-T SET CLOCK**03/18/04 2:15PM**
2 [÷] **3** [×] **2** [ENTER]	2/3*2 1

Your first reaction to this example is that the graphing calculator has produced a wrong answer. But you have set it to round to 0 decimal places (the nearest whole number), so for this setting the answer is correct. If you set rounding (decimals displayed) to 0 and then forget to reset it for later calculations, you may be surprised by some of your answers! With mode set to the default setting of *Float*, the result will be:

Press	Result
2 [÷] **3** [×] **2** [ENTER]	2/3*2 1.333333333

Setting the graphing window

To obtain the best view of the graph, you may need to change the boundaries of the window.

To display the WINDOW Editor, press [WINDOW].

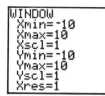

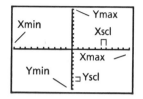

Window variables (shown in WINDOW Editor)

Corresponding viewing window (shown on Graph window)

The *Xmin*, *Xmax*, *Ymin*, and *Ymax* variables represent the boundaries of the viewing window.

Xmin: the minimum value of X to be displayed.
Xmax: the maximum value of X to be displayed.
Ymin: the minimum value of Y to be displayed.
Ymax: the maximum value of Y to be displayed.
Xcsl (X scale): the distance between the tick marks on the X axis.
Yscl (Y scale): the distance between the tick marks on the Y axis.
Xres: pixel resolution—not usually changed except by advanced users.

To change the values:

1. Move the cursor to highlight the value you want to change.

2. Do one of the following:

   • Type a value or an expression. The old value is erased when you begin typing.

   — or —

   • Press [CLEAR] to clear the old value; then type the new one.

3. Press [ENTER], [▼], or [▲].

   Note: Values are stored as you type them; you do not need to press [ENTER]. Pressing [ENTER] simply moves the cursor to the next window variable.

4. After you have made all changes, press [2nd] [QUIT] to close the WINDOW Editor (or [GRAPH] to display the graph).

Example: Change the window settings to display a maximum X value of 25, a minimum X value of -25, a maximum Y value of 50, and a minimum Y value of -50.

Press	Result
[WINDOW]	WINDOW Xmin=-10 Xmax=10 Xscl=1 Ymin=-10 Ymax=10 Yscl=1 Xres=1
[(-)] 2 5 [▼] 2 5 [▼] [▼] [(-)] 5 0 [▼] 5 0	WINDOW Xmin=-25 Xmax=25 Xscl=1 Ymin=-50 Ymax=50 Yscl=1 Xres=1
[2nd] [QUIT]	■

Using ZOOM

The TI-84 Plus has ten predefined window settings that let you quickly adjust the graph window to a predetermined level of magnification. To display this menu, press ZOOM.

Selection	Result
1: ZBox	Lets you draw a box (using the cursor pad) to define the viewing window.
2: Zoom In	After you position the cursor and press ENTER, magnifies the graph around the cursor.
3: Zoom Out	After you position the cursor and press ENTER, displays more of the graph.
4: ZDecimal	Sets the change in X and Y to increments of .1 when you use TRACE.
5: ZSquare	Adjusts the viewing window so that X and Y dimensions are equal.
6: ZStandard	Sets the standard (default) window variables.
7: ZTrig	Sets the built-in trigonometry window variables.
8: ZInteger	After you position the cursor and press ENTER, sets the change in X and Y to whole number increments.
9: ZoomStat	Sets the values for currently defined statistical lists.
0: ZoomFit	Fits **Ymin** and **Ymax** between **Xmin** and **Xmax**.

Building a table

Tables are useful tools for comparing values for a function at multiple points.

Example: Build a table to evaluate the function $Y = X^3 - 2X$ at each integer between -10 and 10.

Press	Result
[MODE] ▼ ▼ ▼ [ENTER] (sets function graphing mode)	**NORMAL** SCI ENG **FLOAT** 0 1 2 3 4 5 6 7 8 9 **RADIAN** DEGREE **FUNC** PAR POL SEQ **CONNECTED** DOT **SEQUENTIAL** SIMUL **REAL** a+bi re^θi **FULL** HORIZ G-T SET CLOCK**03/18/04 2:16PM**
[Y=]	Plot1 Plot2 Plot3 \Y1=■ \Y2= \Y3= \Y4= \Y5= \Y6= \Y7=
[X,T,Θ,n] [MATH] **3** [-] **2** [X,T,Θ,n]	Plot1 Plot2 Plot3 \Y1◼X³-2X■ \Y2= \Y3= \Y4= \Y5= \Y6= \Y7=

[2nd] [TBLSET]	TABLE SETUP
	  TblStart=0
	  △Tbl=1
	Indpnt: **Auto** Ask
	Depend: **Auto** Ask

[(-)] **1 0** [ENTER]
(sets TblStart; default settings shown for the other fields are appropriate)
	TABLE SETUP
	  TblStart=-10
	  △Tbl=1
	Indpnt: **Auto** Ask
	Depend: **Auto** Ask

Press	Result
[2nd] [TABLE]	X | Y1
	-10 | -980
	-9 | -711
	-8 | -496
	-7 | -329
	-6 | -204
	-5 | -115
	-4 | -56
	X=-10

Note: Press ⊡ repeatedly to see the changes in X and Y.

Clearing the Y= Editor

Before proceeding with the remaining examples in this guidebook, clear the Y= Editor.

Press	Result
[Y=]	Plot1 Plot2 Plot3
	\Y1◼X³-2X◼
	\Y2=
	\Y3=
	\Y4=
	\Y5=
	\Y6=
	\Y7=
[CLEAR]	Plot1 Plot2 Plot3
	\Y1=◼
	\Y2=
	\Y3=
	\Y4=
	\Y5=
	\Y6=
	\Y7=

Using the CATALOG

The CATALOG is an alphabetic list of all functions and instructions on the TI-84 Plus. Some of these items are also available on keys and menus.

To select from the CATALOG:

1. Position the cursor where you want to insert the item.
2. Press [2nd] [CATALOG].
3. Press ▽ or △ to move the ▶ indicator to the function or instruction. (You can move quickly down the list by typing the first letter of the item you need.)
4. Press [ENTER]. Your selection is pasted on the home screen.

Notes:

- Items are listed in alphabetical order. Those that do not start with a letter (+, ≥, √, π, and so on) are at the end of the list.
- You can also paste from the CATALOG to an editor, such as the Y= Editor.

Example: Enter the **rand** function on the home screen.

Press	Result	
[2nd] [CATALOG] [R] ▽	CATALOG ▣ Radian ▶rand randBin(randInt(randM(randNorm(re^θi	The ▣ indicates that Alpha-lock is on.
[ENTER]	rand■	

Performing simple calculations

Changing a decimal to a fraction

Example: Add 1/2 + 1/4 and change your answer to a fraction.

Press	Result
1 ⌹ 2 ⊞ 1 ⌹ 4 [ENTER]	```1/2+1/4``` ``` .75```

[MATH] 1
[ENTER]
	```1/2+1/4```
	``` .75```
	```Ans►Frac```
	``` 3/4```

Finding the least common multiple

Example: Find the least common multiple of 15 and 24.

Press	Result
[MATH] [▶] [▲] [▲] [ENTER] 1 5 [,] 2 4 [)] [ENTER]	```lcm(15,24)``` ``` 120```

Finding the square root

Example: Find the square root of 256.

Press	Result
[2nd] [√] 2 5 6 [)] [ENTER]	```√(256)``` ``` 16```

Finding the factorial of numbers

Example: Compute the factorials of 5 and of 30.

Press	Result
5 [MATH] [▸] [▸] [▸] **4** [ENTER]	5! 120
3 0 [MATH] [▸] [▸] [▸] **4** [ENTER]	5! 120 30! 2.652528598ᴇ32 ——Scientific notation

Solving trigonometric functions

Example: Find the sine of an angle of 72°.

Press	Result
[SIN] **7 2** [2nd] [ANGLE] [ENTER] [ )] [ENTER]	sin(72°) .9510565163

If you are solving multiple problems using angles, be sure that mode is set to Degree. If you are in Radian mode and do not wish to change the mode, you can use [2nd] [ANGLE] [ENTER] (as you did in this example) to add the degree symbol to the calculation and override the Radian mode setting.

Adding Complex Numbers

Example: Add (3+5ı) + (2-3ı).

Press	Result
(3 + 5 [2nd] [*i*]) + (2 − 3 [2nd] [*i*]) [ENTER]	(3+5*i*)+(2−3*i*) 5+2*i*

Note: The ı character is the second function of [.] (the decimal key).

Using the equation solver

You can use the TI-84 Plus equation solver to solve for a variable in an equation.

Example: Find the roots for the equation $X^2 - 13X - 48 = 0$.

Press	Result

MATH ▲	```MATH NUM CPX PRB```
	```4↑³√(```
	```5: ˣ√```
	```6:fMin(```
	```7:fMax(```
	```8:nDeriv(```
	```9:fnInt(```
	```0:Solver...```

ENTER	```EQUATION SOLVER``` ```eqn:0=```

If you do not see **eqn:0=** as shown above, press ▲ (the up arrow), and then press CLEAR to erase the existing equation.

Press	Result
X,T,Θ,*n* x² − **1 3** X,T,Θ,*n* − **4 8**	```EQUATION SOLVER``` ```eqn:0=X²-13X-48```

ENTER	```X²-13X-48=0```
	``` X=0```
	``` bound={-1ᴇ99,1…```

Press	Result
[ALPHA] [SOLVE]	X²-13X-48=0 ∎ X=⁻3 bound={⁻1ᴇ99,1… ∎ left-rt=0
1 0 0	X²-13X-48=0 X=100∎ bound={⁻1ᴇ99,1… left-rt=0
[ALPHA] [SOLVE]	X²-13X-48=0 ∎ X=16 bound={⁻1ᴇ99,1… ∎ left-rt=0

The two roots are ⁻3 and 16. Since you did not enter a guess, the TI-84 Plus used 0 (the default guess) and first returned the answer nearest 0. To find other roots, you must enter another guess. In this example, you entered 100.

Entering data into lists

You can enter data into lists using either of two methods:

- Using braces and [STO▸] on the home screen

  — or —

- Using the statistical list editor.

Using [STO▸]

Example: Store 1, 2, 3, and 4 to list 1 (L1).

Press	Result
[2nd] [{] **1** [,] **2** [,] **3** [,] **4** [2nd] [}]	{1,2,3,4}
[STO▸]	{1,2,3,4}→■
[2nd] [L1] [ENTER]	{1,2,3,4}→L1 {1 2 3 4}

Using the statistical list editor

Example: Store 5, 6, 7, and 8 to list 2 (L2).

Press	Result
[STAT] [ENTER]	

Press	Result
▷ △ CLEAR ENTER (if L2 already contains data)	
5 ENTER 6 ENTER 7 ENTER 8 ENTER	
2nd [QUIT] 2nd [L2] ENTER (displays the contents of the list on the home screen)	L2 {5 6 7 8}

Plotting data

When you have statistical data stored in lists, you can display the data you have collected in a scatter plot, xyLine, histogram, box plot, or normal probability plot.

You will need to:

1. Determine which lists contain your data.
2. Tell the TI-84 Plus which lists of data you want to plot and define the plot.
3. Display the plot.

Determine which lists contain your data

Press	Result
[STAT]	**EDIT** CALC TESTS **1:**Edit… 2:SortA(3:SortD(4:ClrList 5:SetUpEditor
[ENTER]	L1 L2 L3 2 1 5 2 6 3 7 4 8 ------ ------ L2(1)=5

Note: In some cases, you may have several lists stored and you may have to press ▶ several times to find the correct lists.

Tell the TI-84 Plus which lists you want to plot

Press	Result
[2nd] [STAT PLOT]	**STAT PLOTS** **1:**Plot1…On L1 L2 □ 2:Plot2…On L1 L2 □ 3:Plot3…Off L1 L2 □ 4↓PlotsOff

Press	Result
4 [ENTER] (turns plots off if any plots are on)	``` PlotsOff Done ■ ```
[2nd] [STAT PLOT]	**STAT PLOTS** 1■Plot1…Off ∟ L1 L2 ■ 2:Plot2…Off ∟ L1 L2 ■ 3:Plot3…Off ∟ L1 L2 ■ 4↓PlotsOff
[ENTER]	**Plot1** Plot2 Plot3 On **Off** Type: ■■ ∠ ╓╜┑ ╫ ╫ ∠ Xlist:L1 Ylist:L2 Mark: ■ + ·
[ENTER] (turns Plot1 on)	**Plot1** Plot2 Plot3 **On** Off Type: ■■ ∠ ╓╜┑ ╫ ╫ ∠ Xlist:L1 Ylist:L2 Mark: ■ + ·
[▼] [▼] [2nd] [LIST] [ENTER] (enters L1 as the Xlist)	**Plot1** Plot2 Plot3 **On** Off Type: ■■ ∠ ╓╜┑ ╫ ╫ ∠ Xlist:L1 Ylist:L2 Mark: ■ + ·
[▼] [2nd] [LIST] [▼] [ENTER] (enters L2 as the Ylist)	**Plot1** Plot2 Plot3 **On** Off Type: ■■ ∠ ╓╜┑ ╫ ╫ ∠ Xlist:L1 Ylist:L2 Mark: ■ + ·

Press	Result
⊡ ▷ [ENTER] (selects + as the plotting mark)	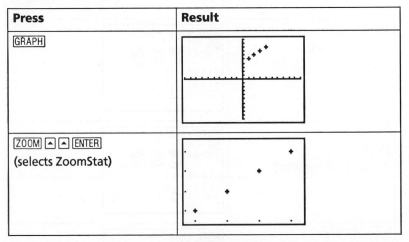
[Y=] [CLEAR]	

Note: This step is optional and is not necessary unless there is a previous entry in the Y= Editor. If there are additional entries in the Y= Editor, press ⊡ [CLEAR] until all are clear.

Display the plot

Press	Result
[GRAPH]	
[ZOOM] ⊞ ⊞ [ENTER] (selects ZoomStat)	

Note: If you would like to add the regression line to a scatter plot, add Y1 to the end of the instruction **LinReg(ax+b) L1, L2, Y1** in *Calculating a linear regression*. (Press [VARS] ▷ [ENTER] [ENTER] to add Y1.) Press [GRAPH] to see the regression line.

Calculating a linear regression

If you wish to calculate the linear regression for data, you can do so using the **LinReg** instruction from the STAT CALC menu.

Example: Calculate the linear regression for the data entered in L1 and L2.

Press	Result
STAT ▶ ▼ ▼ ▼	```EDIT CALC TESTS 1:1-Var Stats 2:2-Var Stats 3:Med-Med 4:LinReg(ax+b) 5:QuadReg 6:CubicReg 7↓QuartReg```
ENTER	```LinReg(ax+b) ■```
2nd [L1] , 2nd [L2]	```LinReg(ax+b) L₁, L₂■```
ENTER	```LinReg y=ax+b a=1 b=4 ■```

Note: The last screen indicates that the line of best fit for the data in lists L1 and L2 is calculated to be y=x+4, where slope is equal to 1 and y-intercept is equal to 4.

Calculating statistical variables

The TI-84 Plus lets you easily calculate one-variable or two-variable statistics for data that you have entered into lists.

Example: Using the data that you entered into L1 from the previous section "Using [STO▸]", calculate one-variable statistics.

Press	Result
[STAT] [▶]	EDIT **CALC** TESTS **1**1-Var Stats 2:2-Var Stats 3:Med-Med 4:LinReg(ax+b) 5:QuadReg 6:CubicReg 7↓QuartReg
[ENTER]	1-Var Stats
[2nd] [L1]	1-Var Stats L₁
[ENTER]	1-Var Stats x̄=2.5 Σx=10 Σx²=30 Sx=1.290994449 σx=1.118033989 ↓n=4

Using the MATRIX Editor

Creating a new matrix

Press	Result
| [2nd] [MATRIX] [◄] | ```
NAMES MATH EDIT
1▪[A]
2:[B]
3:[C]
4:[D]
5:[E]
6:[F]
7↓[G]
``` |
| [ENTER] | ```
MATRIX[A] 1 ×1
[ 0           ]
``` |
| **2** [ENTER] **2** [ENTER] | ```
MATRIX[A] 2 ×2
[ 0    0      ]
[ 0    0      ]


1,1=0
``` |
| **1** [ENTER] **5** [ENTER]<br>**2** [ENTER] **8** [ENTER] | ```
MATRIX[A] 2 ×2
[ 1    5      ]
[ 2    8      ]


2,2=
``` |

Note: When you press [ENTER], the cursor automatically highlights the next cell so that you can continue entering or editing values. To enter a new value, you can start typing without pressing [ENTER], but you must press [ENTER] to edit an existing value.

Using matrices to solve systems of equations

You can solve several equations simultaneously by entering their coefficients into a matrix and then using the **rref** (reduced row-echelon form) function. For example, in the equations below, enter 3, 3, and 24 (for 3X, 3Y, and 24) in the first row, and 2, 1, 13 (for 2X, 1Y, and 13) in the second row.

Example: Solve 3X + 3Y = 24 and 2X + Y = 13

Press	Result
[2nd] [MATRIX] ▶ ▶ ▼	NAMES MATH **EDIT** 1:[A] 2×2 **2**:[B] 3:[C] 4:[D] 5:[E] 6:[F] 7↓[G]
[ENTER]	MATRIX[B] 1 ×1 [0]
2 [ENTER] 3 [ENTER]	MATRIX[B] 2 ×3 [0 0 0] [0 0 0] 1,1=0
3 [ENTER] 3 [ENTER] 2 4 [ENTER] 2 [ENTER] 1 [ENTER] 1 3 [ENTER]	MATRIX[B] 2 ×3 [3 3 24] [2 1 13] 2,3=13
[2nd] [QUIT]	■
[2nd] [MATRIX] ▶	NAMES **MATH** EDIT **1**:det(2:T 3:dim(4:Fill(5:identity(6:randM(7↓augment(

Press	Result
▲ ▲ ▲ ▲ ▲	NAMES **MATH** EDIT 0↑cumSum(A:ref(**B**:rref(C:rowSwap(D:row+(E:*row(F:*row+(
[ENTER]	rref(
[2nd] [MATRIX] [▼] [ENTER]	rref([B]■
[ENTER]	rref([B] [[1 0 5] [0 1 3]]

You can interpret the resulting matrix as:

[1 0 5] represents $1X + 0Y = 5$ or $X = 5$

[0 1 3] represents $0X + 1Y = 3$ or $Y = 3$

The solution to this system of equations is $X = 5$, $Y = 3$.

Grouping

Grouping lets you make a copy of two or more variables and store them in the Flash memory of the TI-84 Plus. This function is similar to "zipping" a computer file and storing it. For example, suppose that you want to save data you collected for time, temperature, humidity, and barometric pressure because you may need to use the data for another assignment.

Grouping lets you keep these lists together for future use. Instead of trying to locate the correct lists and remember which ones were collected together, you can simply recall the group. Grouping also saves space on your graphing calculator by copying variables from RAM to Flash memory.

Example: Group lists L1, L2, and L3 and name them GROUPA.

Press	Result
[2nd] [MEM]	**MEMORY** 2↑Mem Mgmt/Del… 3:Clear Entries 4:ClrAllLists 5:Archive 6:UnArchive 7:Reset… 8:Group…
8	**GROUP** UNGROUP 1▓Create New
[ENTER]	GROUP Name=▓ Caution: You are in alpha mode.
[G] [R] [O] [U] [P] [A]	GROUP Name=GROUPA

Press	Result
[ENTER]	**GROUP** **1:**All+... 2:All-... 3:Prgm... 4:List... 5:GDB... 6:Pic... 7↓Matrix...

4	**SELECT** DONE
	▶ L₁ LIST
	   L₂ LIST
	   L₃ LIST
	   L₄ LIST
	   L₅ LIST
	   L₆ LIST

[ENTER] [▼] [ENTER]
[▼] [ENTER]
	SELECT DONE
	▪ L₁ LIST
	▪ L₂ LIST
	▪ L₃ LIST
	◆ L₄ LIST
	   L₅ LIST
	   L₆ LIST

[▶]	SELECT **DONE** **1:**Done
[ENTER]	Copying Variables to Group: GROUPA Done

Ungrouping

To use variables that have been grouped, you must ungroup.

Example: Ungroup GROUPA.

Press	Result
[2nd] [MEM]	**MEMORY** **2**↑Mem Mgmt/Del… 3:Clear Entries 4:ClrAllLists 5:Archive 6:UnArchive 7:Reset… 8:Group…
8	**GROUP** UNGROUP **1**:Create New
▶	GROUP **UNGROUP** **1**:*GROUPA
[ENTER]	**DuplicateName** **1**:Rename 2:Overwrite 3:Overwrite All 4:Omit 5:Quit L₁ LIST
3 (to overwrite all three lists)	Ungrouping: GROUPA L₁ LIST L₂ LIST ▶ L₃ LIST Done

Error messages

Occasionally, when you enter a function or instruction or attempt to display a graph, the TI-84 Plus will return an error message.

For more details, see Appendix B

Example: Enter the least common multiple function **lcm(** followed by only one number.

Press	Result
[MATH] [▸] [▲] [▲] [ENTER] **2 7** [,]	```lcm(27,```

[ENTER]	```ERR:SYNTAX```
	 ```1■Quit```
	 ```2:Goto```

If you select **1:Quit**, you return to the home screen with the cursor on a new entry line. If you select **2:Goto**, you return to the original entry line; the cursor is flashing at the location of the error. You can now correct the error and continue.

You can find a complete list of error conditions with explanations in Appendix B: General Information.

Resetting defaults

If you are getting unexpected results, or if another person has used your TI-84 Plus and may have changed the settings, you should consider resetting defaults on the TI-84 Plus.

Press	Result
[2nd] [MEM]	**MEMORY** **1:**About 2:Mem Mgmt/Del… 3:Clear Entries 4:ClrAllLists 5:Archive 6:UnArchive 7↓Reset…
7	**RAM ARCHIVE ALL** **1:**All RAM… 2:Defaults…
2	**RESET DEFAULTS** **1:**No 2:Reset
2	TI-84 Plus Silver Edition 2.30 Defaults set

WARNING: If you reset All RAM in step 3 above, you will delete stored variables, lists, and programs. Be sure you have backed up any essential data before you select this option.

Installing applications

Graphing calculator software applications (Apps) let you update the functionality of your TI-84 Plus by installing Apps. This is similar to the way that you add new features to your computer by installing new software applications.

You can find applications for the TI-84 Plus at the TI Online Store at **education.ti.com**. Once you have downloaded an application to your computer, you must use TI Connect™ or TI-GRAPH LINK™ software and the USB computer cable or TI Connectivity Cable USB to install the application on your TI-84 Plus.

Instructions for Windows®

1. Connect the USB computer cable between your computer and TI-84 Plus. Make sure the TI-84 Plus is on the home screen.

2. Using Windows Explorer, locate the application file you want to transfer to the connected device.

3. Reduce the size of the Explorer window so you can see the TI Connect desktop icon.

4. Click the application file you want to transfer.

5. Drag the application file out of Explorer and drop it on the TI Connect desktop icon.

Instructions for Macintosh®

1. Connect the TI Connectivity Cable USB for Macintosh/Windows between your computer and TI-84 Plus, and make sure the TI-84 Plus is on the home screen.

2. Launch the TI Connect for Mac® software and establish a connection to your TI-84 Plus.

3. Drag the application to the TI-84 Plus window in TI-GRAPH LINK. Follow any on-screen instructions that are given.

Running applications

Once you have installed an application on your TI-84 Plus, you must start the application to use its features.

Example: Start the Catalog Help (CtlgHelp) app on the TI-84 Plus.

Press	Result
APPS	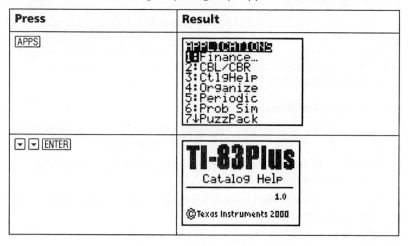
▼ ▼ ENTER	

Quick reference

Press	To
[2nd] [▲]	Darken the screen
[2nd] [▼]	Lighten the screen
[2nd] [▶]	Move the cursor to the end of an expression
[2nd] [◀]	Move the cursor to the beginning of an expression
[ALPHA] [▼]	Page down to the next screen (on menus)
[ALPHA] [▲]	Page up to the next screen (on menus)
[2nd] [ENTRY]	Place your last entry on the current entry line on the home screen
[2nd] [ANS]	Place Ans (a reference to your last answer) on the current entry line on the home screen, allowing you to use the answer in the next calculation
[DEL]	Delete the character under the cursor
[2nd] [INS]	Insert additional characters at the cursor
[▼] [▲]	Move the cursor from line to line
[▶] [◀]	Move the cursor from character to character within a line
[CLEAR]	Clear the current line. (If the cursor is on a blank line, clears everything on the home screen.)

Battery precautions

Take these precautions when replacing batteries.

- Do not leave batteries within the reach of children.

- Do not mix new and used batteries. Do not mix brands (or types within brands) of batteries.

- Do not mix rechargeable and non-rechargeable batteries.

- Install batteries according to polarity (+ and –) diagrams.

- Do not place non-rechargeable batteries in a battery recharger.

- Properly dispose of used batteries immediately.

- Do not incinerate or dismantle batteries.

Activities

The Quadratic Formula

Entering a Calculation

Use the quadratic formula to solve the quadratic equations
$3x^2 + 5x + 2 = 0$ and $2x^2 - x + 3 = 0$. Begin with the equation
$3x^2 + 5x + 2 = 0$.

1. Press **3** [STO▸] [ALPHA] [A] (above [MATH]) to store the coefficient of the x^2 term.

   `3→A:5→B:2→C█`

2. Press [ALPHA] [:] (above [.]). The colon allows you to enter more than one instruction on a line.

3. Press **5** [STO▸] [ALPHA] [B] (above [APPS]) to store the coefficient of the X term. Press [ALPHA] [:] to enter a new instruction on the same line. Press **2** [STO▸] [ALPHA] [C] (above [PRGM]) to store the constant.

4. Press [ENTER] to store the values to the variables A, B, and C.

   `3→A:5→B:2→C`
   `█                    2`

   The last value you stored is shown on the right side of the display. The cursor moves to the next line, ready for your next entry.

5. Press [(] [(-)] [ALPHA] [B] [+] [2nd] [√] [ALPHA] [B] [x^2] [−] **4** [ALPHA] [A] [ALPHA] [C] [)] [)] [÷] [(] **2** [ALPHA] [A] [)] to enter the expression for one of the solutions for the quadratic formula,

   `(-B+√(B²−4AC))/(`
   `2A)█`

$$\frac{-b \pm \sqrt{b^2 - 4ac}}{2a}$$

6. Press ENTER to find one solution for the equation $3x^2 + 5x + 2 = 0$.

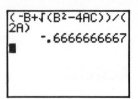

The answer is shown on the right side of the display. The cursor moves to the next line, ready for you to enter the next expression.

Converting to a Fraction

You can show the solution as a fraction.

1. Press MATH to display the **MATH** menu.

```
MATH NUM CPX PRB
1▶▶Frac
2:▶Dec
3: 3
4: 3√(
5: ×√
6: fMin(
7↓fMax(
```

2. Press **1** to select **1:▶Frac** from the **MATH** menu.

When you press **1**, **Ans▶Frac** is displayed on the home screen. **Ans** is a variable that contains the last calculated answer.

```
(-B+√(B²-4AC))/(
2A)
         -.6666666667
Ans▶Frac█
```

3. Press ENTER to convert the result to a fraction.

To save keystrokes, you can recall the last expression you entered, and then edit it for a new calculation.

4. Press 2nd [ENTRY] (above ENTER) to recall the fraction conversion entry, and then press 2nd [ENTRY] again to recall the quadratic-formula expression,

$$\frac{-b + \sqrt{b^2 - 4ac}}{2a}$$

```
(-B+√(B²-4AC))/(
2A)
         -.6666666667
Ans▶Frac
              -2/3
(-B+√(B²-4AC))/(
2A)█
```

---

5. Press ▲ to move the cursor onto the **+** sign in the formula. Press ⊟ to edit the quadratic-formula expression to become:

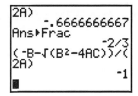

$$\frac{-b-\sqrt{b^2-4ac}}{2a}$$

6. Press [ENTER] to find the other solution for the quadratic equation $3x^2 + 5x + 2 = 0$.

Displaying Complex Results

Now solve the equation $2x^2 - x + 3 = 0$. When you set **a+b**i complex number mode, the TI-84 Plus displays complex results.

1. Press [MODE] ⬇ ⬇ ⬇ ⬇ ⬇ ⬇ (6 times), and then press ▶ to position the cursor over **a+b**i. Press [ENTER] to select **a+b**i complex-number mode.

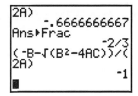

2. Press [2nd] [QUIT] (above [MODE]) to return to the home screen, and then press [CLEAR] to clear it.

3. Press **2** [STO▸] [ALPHA] [A] [ALPHA] [:] [(-)] **1** [STO▸] [ALPHA] [B] [ALPHA] [:] **3** [STO▸] [ALPHA] [C] [ENTER].

The coefficient of the x^2 term, the coefficient of the X term, and the constant for the new equation are stored to A, B, and C, respectively.

4. Press [2nd] [ENTRY] to recall the store instruction, and then press [2nd] [ENTRY] again to recall the quadratic-formula expression,

$$\frac{-b-\sqrt{b^2-4ac}}{2a}$$

5. Press [ENTER] to find one solution for the equation $2x^2 - x + 3 = 0$.

---

6. Press [2nd] [ENTRY] repeatedly until this quadratic-formula expression is displayed:

$$\frac{-b + \sqrt{b^2 - 4ac}}{2a}$$

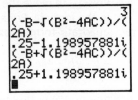

7. Press [ENTER] to find the other solution for the quadratic equation: $2x^2 - x + 3 = 0$.

Note: An alternative for solving equations for real numbers is to use the built-in Equation Solver.

Box with Lid

Defining a Function

Take a 20 cm × 25 cm. sheet of paper and cut X × X squares from two corners. Cut X × 12½ cm rectangles from the other two corners as shown in the diagram below. Fold the paper into a box with a lid. What value of X would give your box the maximum volume V? Use the table and graphs to determine the solution.

Begin by defining a function that describes the volume of the box.

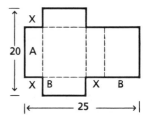

From the diagram:
$2X + A = 20$
$2X + 2B = 25$
$V = A*B*X$

Substituting:
$V = (20 - 2X)(25/2 - X)X$

1. Press $\boxed{Y=}$ to display the **Y=** editor, which is where you define functions for tables and graphing.

2. Press $\boxed{(}$ **20** $\boxed{-}$ **2** $\boxed{X,T,\Theta,n}$ $\boxed{)}$ $\boxed{(}$ **25** $\boxed{\div}$ **2** $\boxed{-}$ $\boxed{X,T,\Theta,n}$ $\boxed{)}$ $\boxed{X,T,\Theta,n}$ $\boxed{ENTER}$ to define the volume function as **Y1** in terms of **X**.

   $\boxed{X,T,\Theta,n}$ lets you enter **X** quickly, without having to press $\boxed{ALPHA}$. The highlighted **=** sign indicates that **Y1** is selected.

   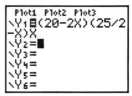

Defining a Table of Values

The table feature of the TI-84 Plus displays numeric information about a function. You can use a table of values from the function you just defined to estimate an answer to the problem.

1. Press [2nd] [TBLSET] (above [WINDOW]) to display the **TABLE SETUP** menu.

2. Press [ENTER] to accept **TblStart=0**.

3. Press **1** [ENTER] to define the table increment **ΔTbl=1**. Leave **Indpnt: Auto** and **Depend: Auto** so that the table will be generated automatically.

4. Press [2nd] [TABLE] (above [GRAPH]) to display the table.

   Notice that the maximum value for **Y1** (box's volume) occurs when **X** is about **4**, between **3** and **5**.

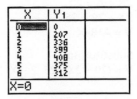

5. Press and hold [▾] to scroll the table until a negative result for **Y1** is displayed.

   Notice that the maximum length of **X** for this problem occurs where the sign of **Y1** (box's volume) changes from positive to negative, between **10** and **11**.

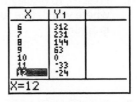

6. Press [2nd] [TBLSET].

   Notice that **TblStart** has changed to **6** to reflect the first line of the table as it was last displayed. (In step 5, the first value of **X** displayed in the table is **6**.)

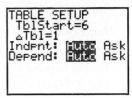

Zooming In on the Table

You can adjust the way a table is displayed to get more information about a defined function. With smaller values for △**Tbl**, you can zoom in on the table.

1. Press **3** [ENTER] to set **TblStart**. Press [.] **1** [ENTER] to set △**Tbl**.

   This adjusts the table setup to get a more accurate estimate of **X** for maximum volume **Y1**.

2. Press [2nd] [TABLE].

3. Press [▼] and [▲] to scroll the table.

   Notice that the maximum value for **Y1** is **410.26**, which occurs at **X=3.7**. Therefore, the maximum occurs where **3.6<X<3.8**.

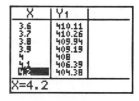

4. Press [2nd] [TBLSET]. Press **3** [.] **6** [ENTER] to set **TblStart**. Press [.] **01** [ENTER] to set △**Tbl**.

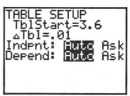

5. Press [2nd] [TABLE], and then press [▼] and [▲] to scroll the table.

   Four equivalent maximum values are shown, **410.26** at **X=3.67, 3.68, 3.69,** and **3.70**.

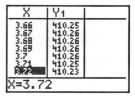

6. Press [▼] or [▲] to move the cursor to **3.67**. Press [▶] to move the cursor into the **Y1** column.

   The value of **Y1** at **X=3.67** is displayed on the bottom line in full precision as **410.261226**.

---

7. Press ▼ to display the other maximum.

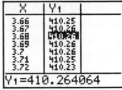

The value of **Y1** at **X=3.68** in full precision is **410.264064**, at **X=3.69** is **410.262318** and at **X=3.7** is **410.256**.

The maximum volume of the box would occur at **3.68** if you could measure and cut the paper at .01-centimeter increments.

Setting the Viewing Window

You also can use the graphing features of the TI-84 Plus to find the maximum value of a previously defined function. When the graph is activated, the viewing window defines the displayed portion of the coordinate plane. The values of the window variables determine the size of the viewing window.

1. Press WINDOW to display the window editor, where you can view and edit the values of the window variables.

The standard window variables define the viewing window as shown. **Xmin**, **Xmax**, **Ymin**, and **Ymax** define the boundaries of the display. **Xscl** and **Yscl** define the distance between tick marks on the **X** and **Y** axes. **Xres** controls resolution.

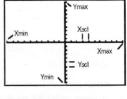

2. Press **0** ENTER to define **Xmin**.

3. Press **20** ÷ **2** to define **Xmax** using an expression.

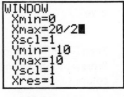

4. Press ENTER. The expression is evaluated, and **10** is stored in **Xmax**. Press ENTER to accept **Xscl** as **1**.

5. Press **0** ENTER **500** ENTER **100** ENTER **1** ENTER to define the remaining window variables.

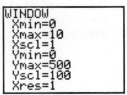

Displaying and Tracing the Graph

Now that you have defined the function to be graphed and the window in which to graph it, you can display and explore the graph. You can trace along a function using the **TRACE** feature.

1. Press GRAPH to graph the selected function in the viewing window.

   The graph of **Y1=(20-2X)(25/2-X)X** is displayed.

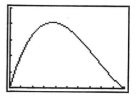

2. Press ▶ to activate the free-moving graph cursor.

   The **X** and **Y** coordinate values for the position of the graph cursor are displayed on the bottom line.

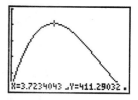

3. Press ◀, ▶, ▲, and ▼ to move the free-moving cursor to the apparent maximum of the function.

   As you move the cursor, the **X** and **Y** coordinate values are updated continually.

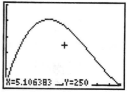

4. Press TRACE. The trace cursor is displayed on the **Y1** function.

   The function that you are tracing is displayed in the top-left corner.

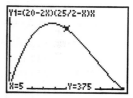

5. Press ◀ and ▶ to trace along **Y1**, one **X** dot at a time, evaluating **Y1** at each **X**.

   You also can enter your estimate for the maximum value of **X**.

6. Press **3** □ **8**. When you press a number key while in **TRACE**, the **X=** prompt is displayed in the bottom-left corner.

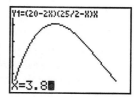

---

7. Press ENTER.

   The trace cursor jumps to the point on the **Y1** function evaluated at **X=3.8**.

   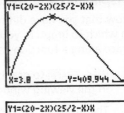

8. Press ◄ and ► until you are on the maximum **Y** value.

   This is the maximum of **Y1(X)** for the **X** pixel values. The actual, precise maximum may lie between pixel values.

   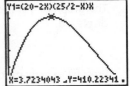

Zooming In on the Graph

To help identify maximums, minimums, roots, and intersections of functions, you can magnify the viewing window at a specific location using the **ZOOM** instructions.

1. Press ZOOM to display the **ZOOM** menu.

   This menu is a typical TI-84 Plus menu. To select an item, you can either press the number or letter next to the item, or you can press ▼ until the item number or letter is highlighted, and then press ENTER.

   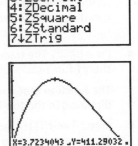

2. Press **2** to select **2:Zoom In**.

   The graph is displayed again. The cursor has changed to indicate that you are using a **ZOOM** instruction.

3. With the cursor near the maximum value of the function, press ENTER.

   The new viewing window is displayed. Both **Xmax–Xmin** and **Ymax–Ymin** have been adjusted by factors of 4, the default values for the zoom factors.

   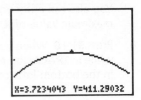

4. Press [WINDOW] to display the new window settings.

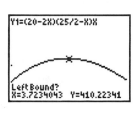
```
WINDOW
 Xmin=2.4734042…
 Xmax=4.9734042…
 Xscl=1
 Ymin=348.79032…
 Ymax=473.79032…
 Yscl=100
 Xres=1
```

Finding the Calculated Maximum

You can use a **CALCULATE** menu operation to calculate a local maximum of a function.

1. Press [2nd] [CALC] (above [TRACE]) to display the **CALCULATE** menu. Press **4** to select **4:maximum**.

   The graph is displayed again with a **Left Bound?** prompt.

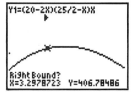
```
Y1=(20-2X)(25/2-X)X



Left Bound?
X=3.7234043   Y=410.22341
```

2. Press [◄] to trace along the curve to a point to the left of the maximum, and then press [ENTER].

   A ▶ at the top of the screen indicates the selected bound.

   A **Right Bound?** prompt is displayed.

```
Y1=(20-2X)(25/2-X)X
       ▶


Right Bound?
X=3.2978723   Y=406.78486
```

3. Press [►] to trace along the curve to a point to the right of the maximum, and then press [ENTER].

   A ◄ at the top of the screen indicates the selected bound.

   A **Guess?** prompt is displayed.

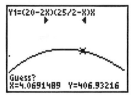
```
Y1=(20-2X)(25/2-X)X
       ▶      ◄


Guess?
X=4.0691489   Y=406.93216
```

4. Press [◄] to trace to a point near the maximum, and then press [ENTER].

Or, press **3 ⬚ 8**, and then press ENTER to enter a guess for the maximum.

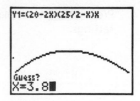

When you press a number key in **TRACE**, the **X=** prompt is displayed in the bottom-left corner.

Notice how the values for the calculated maximum compare with the maximums found with the free-moving cursor, the trace cursor, and the table.

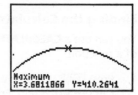

Note: In steps 2 and 3 above, you can enter values directly for Left Bound and Right Bound, in the same way as described in step **4**.

Comparing Test Results Using Box Plots

Problem

An experiment found a significant difference between boys and girls pertaining to their ability to identify objects held in their left hands, which are controlled by the right side of their brains, versus their right hands, which are controlled by the left side of their brains. The TI Graphics team conducted a similar test for adult men and women.

The test involved 30 small objects, which participants were not allowed to see. First, they held 15 of the objects one by one in their left hands and guessed what they were. Then they held the other 15 objects one by one in their right hands and guessed what they were. Use box plots to compare visually the correct-guess data from this table.

Each row in the table represents the results observed for one subject. Note that 10 women and 12 men were tested.

Correct Guesses			
Women Left	Women Right	Men Left	Men Right
8	4	7	12
9	1	8	6
12	8	7	12
11	12	5	12
10	11	7	7
8	11	8	11
12	13	11	12
7	12	4	8
9	11	10	12
11	12	14	11
		13	9
		5	9

Procedure

1. Press STAT **5** to select **5:SetUpEditor**. Enter list names **WLEFT, WRGHT, MLEFT,** and **MRGHT,** separated by commas. Press ENTER. The stat list editor now contains only these four lists.

---

2. Press [STAT] **1** to select **1:Edit**.

3. Enter into **WLEFT** the number of correct guesses each woman made using her left hand (**Women Left**). Press [▶] to move to **WRGHT** and enter the number of correct guesses each woman made using her right hand (**Women Right**).

4. Likewise, enter each man's correct guesses in **MLEFT** (**Men Left**) and **MRGHT** (**Men Right**).

5. Press [2nd] [STAT PLOT]. Select **1:Plot1**. Turn on plot 1; define it as a modified box plot ⊡⋯ that uses **WLEFT**. Move the cursor to the top line and select **Plot2**. Turn on plot 2; define it as a modified box plot that uses **WRGHT**.

6. Press [Y=]. Turn off all functions.

7. Press [WINDOW]. Set **Xscl=1** and **Yscl=0**. Press [ZOOM] **9** to select **9:ZoomStat**. This adjusts the viewing window and displays the box plots for the women's results.

8. Press [TRACE].

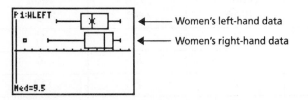

Women's left-hand data
Women's right-hand data

Use [◀] and [▶] to examine **minX, Q1, Med, Q3,** and **maxX** for each plot. Notice the outlier to the women's right-hand data. What is the median for the left hand? For the right hand? With which hand were the women more accurate guessers, according to the box plots?

9. Examine the men's results. Redefine plot 1 to use **MLEFT**, redefine plot 2 to use **MRGHT**. Press [TRACE].

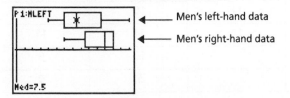

Men's left-hand data
Men's right-hand data

Press [◀] and [▶] to examine **minX, Q1, Med, Q3,** and **maxX** for each plot What difference do you see between the plots?

---

10. Compare the left-hand results. Redefine plot 1 to use **WLEFT**, redefine plot 2 to use **MLEFT**, and then press ⟦TRACE⟧ to examine **minX**, **Q1**, **Med**, **Q3**, and **maxX** for each plot. Who were the better left-hand guessers, men or women?

11. Compare the right-hand results. Define plot 1 to use **WRGHT**, define plot 2 to use **MRGHT**, and then press ⟦TRACE⟧ to examine **minX**, **Q1**, **Med**, **Q3**, and **maxX** for each plot. Who were the better right-hand guessers?

   In the original experiment boys did not guess as well with right hands, while girls guessed equally well with either hand. This is not what our box plots show for adults. Do you think that this is because adults have learned to adapt or because our sample was not large enough?

Graphing Piecewise Functions

Problem

The fine for speeding on a road with a speed limit of 45 kilometers per hour (kph) is 50; plus 5 for each kph from 46 to 55 kph; plus 10 for each kph from 56 to 65 kph; plus 20 for each kph from 66 kph and above. Graph the piecewise function that describes the cost of the ticket.

The fine (Y) as a function of kilometers per hour (X) is:

$Y = 0$	$0 < X \le 45$
$Y = 50 + 5 \, (X - 45)$	$45 < X \le 55$
$Y = 50 + 5 * 10 + 10 \, (X - 55)$	$55 < X \le 65$
$Y = 50 + 5 * 10 + 10 * 10 + 20 \, (X - 65)$	$65 < X$

Procedure

1. Press <kbd>MODE</kbd>. Select **Func** and the default settings.

2. Press <kbd>Y=</kbd>. Turn off all functions and stat plots. Enter the **Y=** function to describe the fine. Use the **TEST** menu operations to define the piecewise function. Set the graph style for **Y1** to $\cdot$ (dot).

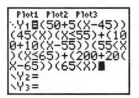

3. Press <kbd>WINDOW</kbd> and set **Xmin=‾2, Xscl=10, Ymin=‾5,** and **Yscl=10**. Ignore **Xmax** and **Ymax**; they are set by ΔX and ΔY in step 4.

4. Press <kbd>2nd</kbd> [QUIT] to return to the home screen. Store **1** to ΔX, and then store **5** to ΔY. ΔX and ΔY are on the **VARS Window X/Y** secondary menu. ΔX and ΔY specify the horizontal and vertical distance between the centers of adjacent pixels. Integer values for ΔX and ΔY produce nice values for tracing.

5. Press <kbd>TRACE</kbd> to plot the function. At what speed does the ticket exceed 250?

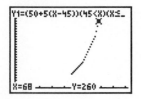

Graphing Inequalities

Problem

Graph the inequality $0.4x^3 - 3x + 5 < 0.2x + 4$. Use the **TEST** menu operations to explore the values of X where the inequality is true and where it is false.

Procedure

1. Press MODE. Select **Dot, Simul**, and the default settings. Setting **Dot** mode changes all graph style icons to ∴ (dot) in the **Y=** editor.

2. Press Y=. Turn off all functions and stat plots. Enter the left side of the inequality as **Y4** and the right side as **Y5**.

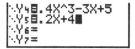

```
∴Y4◻.4X^3-3X+5
∴Y5◻.2X+4▮
∴Y6=
∴Y7=
```

3. Enter the statement of the inequality as **Y6**. This function evaluates to **1** if true or **0** if false.

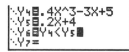

```
∴Y4◻.4X^3-3X+5
∴Y5◻.2X+4
∴Y6◻Y4<Y5▮
∴Y7=
```

4. Press ZOOM 6 to graph the inequality in the standard window.

5. Press TRACE ▼ ▼ to move to **Y6**. Then press ◄ and ► to trace the inequality, observing the value of **Y**.

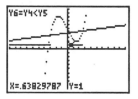

```
Y6=Y4<Y5
```
X=.63829787   Y=1

6. Press Y=. Turn off **Y4, Y5,** and **Y6**. Enter equations to graph only the inequality.

```
∴Y4=.4X^3-3X+5
∴Y5=.2X+4
∴Y6=Y4<Y5
∴Y7◻Y6*Y4
∴Y8◻Y6*Y5
```

7. Press TRACE. Notice that the values of **Y7** and **Y8** are zero where the inequality is false.

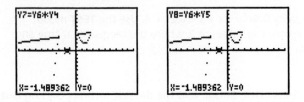

Solving a System of Nonlinear Equations

Problem

Using a graph, solve the equation $x^3-2x=2\cos(x)$. Stated another way, solve the system of two equations and two unknowns: $y = x^3-2x$ and $y = 2\cos(x)$. Use **ZOOM** factors to control the decimal places displayed on the graph.

Procedure

1. Press [MODE]. Select the default mode settings. Press [Y=]. Turn off all functions and stat plots. Enter the functions.

   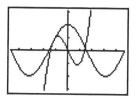

   ```
   \Y₁■X³-2X
   \Y₀■2cos(X)■
   ```

2. Press [ZOOM] 4 to select **4:ZDecimal**. The display shows that two solutions may exist (points where the two functions appear to intersect).

3. Press [ZOOM] [▶] 4 to select **4:SetFactors** from the **ZOOM MEMORY** menu. Set **XFact=10** and **YFact=10**.

4. Press [ZOOM] 2 to select **2:Zoom In**. Use [◀], [▶], [▲], and [▼] to move the free-moving cursor onto the apparent intersection of the functions on the right side of the display. As you move the cursor, notice that the **X** and **Y** values have one decimal place.

5. Press [ENTER] to zoom in. Move the cursor over the intersection. As you move the cursor, notice that now the **X** and **Y** values have two decimal places.

6. Press [ENTER] to zoom in again. Move the free-moving cursor onto a point exactly on the intersection. Notice the number of decimal places.

7. Press [2nd] [CALC] 5 to select **5:intersect**. Press [ENTER] to select the first curve and [ENTER] to select the second curve. To guess, move the trace cursor near the intersection. Press [ENTER]. What are the coordinates of the intersection point?

8. Press [ZOOM] 4 to select **4:ZDecimal** to redisplay the original graph.

---

9. Press $\boxed{\text{ZOOM}}$. Select **2:Zoom In** and repeat steps 4 through 8 to explore the apparent function intersection on the left side of the display.

Using a Program to Create the Sierpinski Triangle

Setting up the Program

This program creates a drawing of a famous fractal, the Sierpinski Triangle, and stores the drawing to a picture. To begin, press PRGM ▶ ▶ 1. Name the program **SIERPINS**, and then press ENTER. The program editor is displayed.

Program

```
PROGRAM:SIERPINS
:FnOff :ClrDraw
:PlotsOff
:AxesOff

:0→Xmin:1→Xmax          ─┐  Set viewing window.
:0→Ymin:1→Ymax          ─┘

:rand→X:rand→Y

:For(K,1,3000)          ─┐  Beginning of For group.
:rand→N                 ─┘

:If N≤1/3                ─┐
:Then                    │
:.5X→X                   ├─ If/Then group
:.5Y→Y                   │
:End                    ─┘

:If 1/3<N and N≤2/3      ─┐
:Then                    │
:.5(.5+X)→X              ├─ If/Then group.
:.5(1+Y)→Y               │
:End                    ─┘

:If 2/3<N                ─┐
:Then                    │
:.5(1+X)→X               ├─ If/Then group.
:.5Y→Y                   │
:End                    ─┘

:Pt-On(X,Y)                 Draw point.
:End                        End of For group.
:StorePic 6                 Store picture.
```

After you execute the program above, you can recall and display the picture with the instruction **RecallPic 6**.

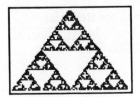

Graphing Cobweb Attractors

Problem

Using **Web** format, you can identify points with attracting and repelling behavior in sequence graphing.

Procedure

1. Press MODE. Select **Seq** and the default mode settings. Press 2nd [FORMAT]. Select **Web** format and the default format settings.

2. Press Y=. Clear all functions and turn off all stat plots. Enter the sequence that corresponds to the expression $Y = K X(1-X)$.

   u(n)=Ku(n-1)(1-u(n-1))
   u(nMin)=.01

3. Press 2nd [QUIT] to return to the home screen, and then store **2.9** to **K**.

4. Press WINDOW. Set the window variables.

nMin=0	Xmin=0	Ymin=⁻.26
nMax=10	Xmax=1	Ymax=1.1
PlotStart=1	Xscl=1	Yscl=1
PlotStep=1		

5. Press TRACE to display the graph, and then press ▶ to trace the cobweb. This is a cobweb with one attractor.

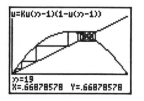

6. Change **K** to **3.44** and trace the graph to show a cobweb with two attractors.

7. Change **K** to **3.54** and trace the graph to show a cobweb with four attractors.

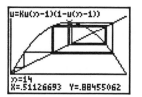

Using a Program to Guess the Coefficients

Setting Up the Program

This program graphs the function A sin(BX) with random integer coefficients between 1 and 10. Try to guess the coefficients and graph your guess as C sin(DX). The program continues until your guess is correct.

Program

```
PROGRAM:GUESS
:PlotsOff :Func
:FnOff :Radian
:ClrHome

:"Asin(BX)"→Y1
:"Csin(DX)"→Y2

:GraphStyle(1,1)
:GraphStyle(2,5)

:FnOff 2

:randInt(1,10)→A
:randInt(1,10)→B
:0→C:0→D

:-2π→Xmin
:2π→Xmax
:π/2→Xscl
:-10→Ymin
:10→Ymax
:1→Yscl

:DispGraph
:Pause

:FnOn 2
:Lbl Z

:Prompt C,D

:DispGraph
:Pause
```

Define equations.

Set line and path graph styles.

Initialize coefficients.

Set viewing window.

Display graph.

Prompt for guess.

Display graph.

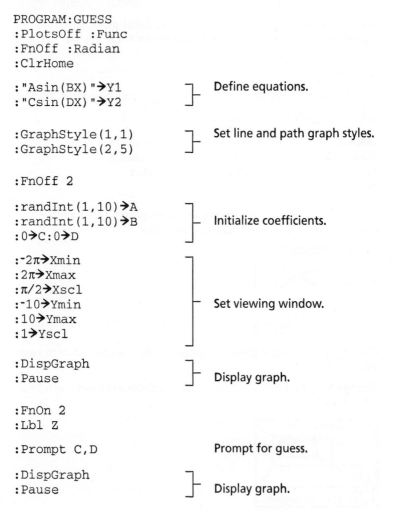

```
:If C=A
:Text(1,1,"C IS OK")
:If C≠A
:Text(1,1,"C IS
WRONG")
:If D=B
:Text(1,50,"D IS OK")
:If D≠B
:Text(1,50,"D IS
WRONG")
```
⎤
⎥
⎥
⎦ — Display results.

```
:DispGraph
:Pause
```
⎤
⎦ — Display graph.

```
:If C=A and D=B
:Stop
:Goto Z
```
⎤
⎦ — Quit if guesses are correct.

Graphing the Unit Circle and Trigonometric Curves

Problem

Using parametric graphing mode, graph the unit circle and the sine curve to show the relationship between them.

Any function that can be plotted in **Func** mode can be plotted in **Par** mode by defining the **X** component as **T** and the **Y** component as **F(T)**.

Procedure

1. Press MODE. Select **Par, Simul,** and the default settings.

2. Press WINDOW. Set the viewing window.

Tmin=0	**Xmin=⁻2**	**Ymin=⁻3**
Tmax=2π	**Xmax=7.4**	**Ymax=3**
Tstep=.1	**Xscl=π/2**	**Yscl=1**

3. Press Y=. Turn off all functions and stat plots. Enter the expressions to define the unit circle centered on (0,0).

4. Enter the expressions to define the sine curve.

5. Press TRACE. As the graph is plotting, you may press ENTER to pause and ENTER again to resume graphing as you watch the sine function "unwrap" from the unit circle.

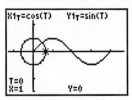

Note: You can generalize the unwrapping. Replace **sin(T)** in **Y2T** with any other trig function to unwrap that function.

Finding the Area between Curves

Problem

Find the area of the region bounded by:

$f(x)$ = $300x/(x^2 + 625)$
$g(x)$ = $3\cos(.1x)$
x = 75

Procedure

1. Press [MODE]. Select the default mode settings.

2. Press [WINDOW]. Set the viewing window.

   Xmin=0   **Ymin=‾5**   **Xres=1**
   Xmax=100   **Ymax=10**
   Xscl=10   **Yscl=1**

3. Press [Y=]. Turn off all functions and stat plots. Enter the upper and lower functions.

   Y1=300X/(X²+625)
   Y2=3cos(.1X)

4. Press [2nd] [CALC] **5** to select **5:Intersect**. The graph is displayed. Select a first curve, second curve, and guess for the intersection toward the left side of the display. The solution is displayed, and the value of **X** at the intersection, which is the lower limit of the integral, is stored in **Ans** and **X**.

5. Press [2nd] [QUIT] to go to the home screen. Press [2nd] [DRAW] **7** and use **Shade(** to see the area graphically.

   Shade(Y2,Y1,Ans,75)

   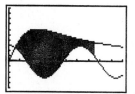

6. Press [2nd] [QUIT] to return to the home screen. Enter the expression to evaluate the integral for the shaded region.

   fnInt(Y1−Y2,X,Ans,75)

   The area is **325.839962**.

Using Parametric Equations: Ferris Wheel Problem

Problem

Using two pairs of parametric equations, determine when two objects in motion are closest to each other in the same plane.

A ferris wheel has a diameter (d) of 20 meters and is rotating counterclockwise at a rate (s) of one revolution every 12 seconds. The parametric equations below describe the location of a ferris wheel passenger at time T, where α is the angle of rotation, (0,0) is the bottom center of the ferris wheel, and (10,10) is the passenger's location at the rightmost point, when T=0.

$X(T) = r \cos \alpha$ where $\alpha = 2\pi Ts$ and $r = d/2$
$Y(T) = r + r \sin \alpha$

A person standing on the ground throws a ball to the ferris wheel passenger. The thrower's arm is at the same height as the bottom of the ferris wheel, but 25 meters (b) to the right of the ferris wheel's lowest point (25,0). The person throws the ball with velocity (v_0) of 22 meters per second at an angle (θ) of 66° from the horizontal. The parametric equations below describe the location of the ball at time T.

$X(T) = b - Tv_0 \cos\theta$
$Y(T) = Tv_0 \sin\theta - (g/2) T^2$ where $g = 9.8$ m/sec^2

Procedure

1. Press MODE. Select **Par, Simul**, and the default settings. **Simul** (simultaneous) mode simulates the two objects in motion over time.

2. Press WINDOW. Set the viewing window.

Tmin=0	Xmin=‑13	Ymin=0
Tmax=12	Xmax=34	Ymax=31
Tstep=.1	Xscl=10	Yscl=10

3. Press Y=. Turn off all functions and stat plots. Enter the expressions to define the path of the ferris wheel and the path of the ball. Set the graph style for **X2T** to ⫟ (path).

Plot1 Plot2 Plot3
\X₁ᴛ■10cos(πT/6)
  Y₁ᴛ■10+10sin(πT
/6)
◦X₂ᴛ■25−22Tcos(6
6°)
  Y₂ᴛ■22Tsin(66°)
−(9.8/2)T²

Note: Try setting the graph styles to ◦⫟ **X1T** and ◦ **X2T**, which simulates a chair on the ferris wheel and the ball flying through the air when you press GRAPH.

4. Press GRAPH to graph the equations. Watch closely as they are plotted. Notice that the ball and the ferris wheel passenger appear to be closest where the paths cross in the top-right quadrant of the ferris wheel.

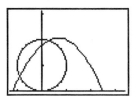

5. Press WINDOW. Change the viewing window to concentrate on this portion of the graph.

Tmin=1	**Xmin=0**	**Ymin=10**
Tmax=3	**Xmax=23.5**	**Ymax=25.5**
Tstep=.03	**Xscl=10**	**Yscl=10**

6. Press TRACE. After the graph is plotted, press ▶ to move near the point on the ferris wheel where the paths cross. Notice the values of **X**, **Y**, and **T**.

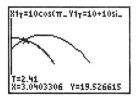

7. Press ▼ to move to the path of the ball. Notice the values of **X** and **Y** (**T** is unchanged). Notice where the cursor is located. This is the position of the ball when the ferris wheel passenger passes the intersection. Did the ball or the passenger reach the intersection first?

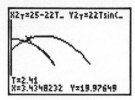

You can use $\boxed{\text{TRACE}}$ to, in effect, take snapshots in time and explore the relative behavior of two objects in motion.

Demonstrating the Fundamental Theorem of Calculus

Problem 1

Using the functions **fnInt(** and **nDeriv(** from the **MATH** menu to graph functions defined by integrals and derivatives demonstrates graphically that:

$$F(x) = \int_1^x dt = \ln(x), x > 0 \text{ and that}$$

$$Dx\left[\int_1^x \frac{1}{t} dt\right] = \frac{1}{x}$$

Procedure 1

1. Press MODE. Select the default settings.

2. Press WINDOW. Set the viewing window.

Xmin=.01	**Ymin=-1.5**	**Xres=3**
Xmax=10	**Ymax=2.5**	
Xscl=1	**Yscl=1**	

3. Press Y=. Turn off all functions and stat plots. Enter the numerical integral of 1/T from 1 to X and the function ln(X). Set the graph style for **Y1** to \ (line) and **Y2** to ↓ (path).

```
Plot1  Plot2  Plot3
\Y1■fnInt(1/T,T,
1,X)
↓Y2■ln(X)
```

4. Press TRACE. Press ◄, ▲, ►, and ▼ to compare the values of **Y1** and **Y2**.

5. Press Y=. Turn off **Y1** and **Y2**, and then enter the numerical derivative of the integral of 1/X and the function 1/X. Set the graph style for **Y3** to \ (line) and **Y4** to ▌ (thick).

```
Plot1  Plot2  Plot3
\Y1=fnInt(1/T,T,
1,X)
↓Y2=ln(X)
\Y3■nDeriv(Y1,X,
X)
▌Y4■1/X
```

---

6. Press [TRACE]. Again, use the cursor keys to compare the values of the two graphed functions, **Y3** and **Y4**.

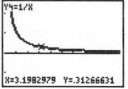

Problem 2

Explore the functions defined by

$$y = \int_2^x t^2\,dt, \quad \int_0^x t^2\,dt, \quad \text{and} \quad \int_2^x t^2\,dt$$

Procedure 2

1. Press [Y=]. Turn off all functions and stat plots. Use a list to define these three functions simultaneously. Store the function in **Y5**.

```
 Plot1 Plot2 Plot3
1,X)
·\Y2=ln(X)
\Y3=nDeriv(Y1,X,
X)
\Y4=1/X
\Y5=fnInt(T²,T,{
-2,0,2},X)
```

2. Press [ZOOM] **6** to select **6:ZStandard**.

3. Press [TRACE]. Notice that the functions appear identical, only shifted vertically by a constant.

4. Press [Y=]. Enter the numerical derivative of **Y5** in **Y6**.

```
 Plot1 Plot2 Plot3
\Y3=nDeriv(Y1,X,
X)
\Y4=1/X
\Y5=fnInt(T²,T,{
-2,0,2},X)
\Y6=nDeriv(Y5,X,
X)
```

5. Press [TRACE]. Notice that although the three graphs defined by **Y5** are different, they share the same derivative.

Activities

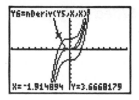

Computing Areas of Regular N-Sided Polygons

Problem

Use the equation solver to store a formula for the area of a regular N-sided polygon, and then solve for each variable, given the other variables. Explore the fact that the limiting case is the area of a circle, πr^2.

Consider the formula $A = NB^2 \sin(\pi/N) \cos(\pi/N)$ for the area of a regular polygon with N sides of equal length and B distance from the center to a vertex.

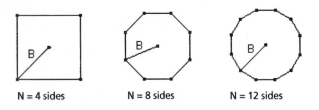

| N = 4 sides | N = 8 sides | N = 12 sides |

Procedure

1. Press MATH **0** to select **0:Solver** from the **MATH** menu. Either the equation editor or the interactive solver editor is displayed. If the interactive solver editor is displayed, press △ to display the equation editor.

2. Enter the formula as **0=A−NB²sin(π / N)cos(π / N)**, and then press ENTER. The interactive solver editor is displayed.

```
A-NB²sin(π/N)…=0
  A=0
  N=0
  B=0
  bound={-1ε99,1…
```

3. Enter **N=4** and **B=6** to find the area (**A**) of a square with a distance (**B**) from center to vertex of 6 centimeters.

4. Press △ △ to move the cursor onto **A**, and then press ALPHA [SOLVE]. The solution for **A** is displayed on the interactive solver editor.

```
A-NB²sin(π/N)…=0
• A=72.000000000…
  N=4
  B=6
  bound={-1ε99,1…
• left-rt=0
```

5. Now solve for **B** for a given area with various number of sides. Enter **A=200** and **N=6**. To find the distance **B**, move the cursor onto **B**, and then press [ALPHA] [SOLVE].

6. Enter **N=8**. To find the distance **B**, move the cursor onto **B**, and then press [ALPHA] [SOLVE]. Find **B** for **N=9**, and then for **N=10**.

Find the area given **B=6**, and **N=10, 100, 150, 1000**, and **10000**. Compare your results with $\pi 6^2$ (the area of a circle with radius 6), which is approximately 113.097.

7. Enter **B=6**. To find the area **A**, move the cursor onto **A**, and then press [ALPHA] [SOLVE]. Find **A** for **N=10**, then **N=100**, then **N=150**, then **N=1000**, and finally **N=10000**. Notice that as **N** gets large, the area **A** approaches πB^2.

Now graph the equation to see visually how the area changes as the number of sides gets large.

8. Press [MODE]. Select the default mode settings.

9. Press [WINDOW]. Set the viewing window.

Xmin=0	Ymin=0	Xres=1
Xmax=200	Ymax=150	
Xscl=10	Yscl=10	

10. Press [Y=]. Turn off all functions and stat plots. Enter the equation for the area. Use **X** in place of **N**. Set the graph styles as shown.

11. Press [TRACE]. After the graph is plotted, press **100** [ENTER] to trace to **X=100**. Press **150** [ENTER]. Press **188** [ENTER]. Notice that as **X** increases, the value of **Y** converges to $\pi 6^2$, which is approximately 113.097. **Y2**=πB^2 (the area of the circle) is a horizontal asymptote to **Y1**. The

area of an N-sided regular polygon, with r as the distance from the center to a vertex, approaches the area of a circle with radius r (πr^2) as N gets large.

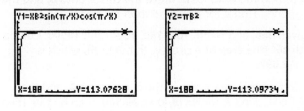

Computing and Graphing Mortgage Payments

Problem

You are a loan officer at a mortgage company, and you recently closed on a 30-year home mortgage at 8 percent interest with monthly payments of 800. The new home owners want to know how much will be applied to the interest and how much will be applied to the principal when they make the 240th payment 20 years from now.

Procedure

1. Press [MODE] and set the fixed-decimal mode to **2** decimal places. Set the other mode settings to the defaults.

2. Press [APPS] [ENTER] [ENTER] to display the **TVM Solver**. Enter these values.

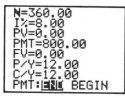

    Note: Enter a positive number (**800**) to show **PMT** as a cash inflow. Payment values will be displayed as positive numbers on the graph. Enter **0** for **FV**, since the future value of a loan is 0 once it is paid in full. Enter **PMT: END**, since payment is due at the end of a period.

3. Move the cursor onto the **PV=** prompt, and then press [ALPHA] [SOLVE]. The present value, or mortgage amount, of the house is displayed at the **PV=** prompt.

```
N=360.00
I%=8.00
•PV=-109026.80
PMT=800.00
FV=0.00
P/Y=12.00
C/Y=12.00
PMT:END BEGIN
```

Now compare the graph of the amount of interest with the graph of the amount of principal for each payment.

4. Press [MODE]. Set **Par** and **Simul**.

5. Press [Y=]. Turn off all functions and stat plots. Enter these equations and set the graph styles as shown.

```
Plot1 Plot2 Plot3
\X₁ₜ◼T
 Y₁ₜ◼ΣPrn(T,T)
\X₂ₜ◼T
 Y₂ₜ◼ΣInt(T,T)
·.X₃ₜ◼T
 Y₃ₜ◼Y₁ₜ+Y₂ₜ
```

Note: **ΣPrn(** and **ΣInt(** are located on the **FINANCE** menu (**APPS 1:FINANCE**).

6. Press [WINDOW]. Set these window variables.

Tmin=1	**Xmin=0**	**Ymin=0**
Tmax=360	**Xmax=360**	**Ymax=1000**
Tstep=12	**Xscl=10**	**Yscl=100**

Note: To increase the graph speed, change **Tstep** to **24**.

7. Press [TRACE]. After the graph is drawn, press **240** [ENTER] to move the trace cursor to **T=240**, which is equivalent to 20 years of payments.

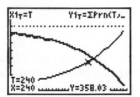

The graph shows that for the 240th payment (**X=240**), 358.03 of the 800 payment is applied to principal (**Y=358.03**).

Note: The sum of the payments (**Y3T=Y1T+Y2T**) is always 800.

8. Press [▼] to move the cursor onto the function for interest defined by **X2T** and **Y2T**. Enter **240**.

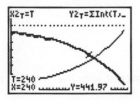

The graph shows that for the 240th payment (**X=240**), 441.97 of the 800 payment is interest (**Y=441.97**).

9. Press [2nd] [QUIT] [APPS] [ENTER] **9** to paste **9:bal(** to the home screen. Check the figures from the graph.

```
bal(239)
                -66295.33
Ans*(.08/12)
                  -441.97
```

At which monthly payment will the principal allocation surpass the interest allocation?

3

Memory and Variable Management

Checking Available Memory

MEMORY Menu

At any time you can check available memory or manage existing memory by selecting items from the **MEMORY** menu. To access this menu, press [2nd] [MEM].

MEMORY

1: About...	Displays information about the graphing calculator including current OS version number.
2: Mem Mgmt/Del...	Reports memory availability and variable usage.
3: Clear Entries	Clears **ENTRY** (last-entry storage).
4: ClrAllLists	Clears all lists in memory.
5: Archive...	Archives a selected variable.
6: UnArchive...	UnArchives a selected variable.
7: Reset...	Displays the **RAM, ARCHIVE**, and **ALL** menus
8: Group...	Displays **GROUP** and **UNGROUP** menus.

To check memory availability, first press [2nd] [MEM] and then select **2:Mem Mgmt/Del**.

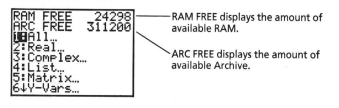

RAM FREE displays the amount of available RAM.

ARC FREE displays the amount of available Archive.

Available RAM, Archive, and App Slots

The TI-84 Plus / TI-84 Plus Silver Edition has Archive, RAM, and Application (App) slot memory for you to use and manage. The available RAM stores computations, lists, variables, and data. The available Archive lets you store programs, Apps, groups, and other variables. The App slots are actually individual sectors of Flash ROM where Apps are stored.

Graphing calculator	Available RAM	Available Archive	App Slots
TI-84 Plus	24 Kilobytes	491 Kilobytes	30
TI-84 Plus Silver Edition	24 Kilobytes	1.5 Megabytes	94

Note: Some Apps take up several App slots.

Displaying the About Screen

About displays information about the TI-84 Plus Operating System (OS) Version, Product Number, Product Identification (ID), and Flash Application (App) Certificate Revision Number. To display the About screen, press [2nd] [MEM] and then select **1:About**.

Displays the type of graphing calculator.

Displays the OS version. As new software upgrades become available, you can electronically upgrade your unit.

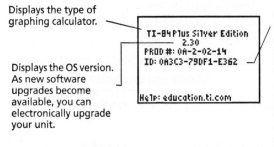

```
TI-84 Plus Silver Edition
        2.30
PROD #: 0A-2-02-14
ID: 0A3C3-79DF1-E362

Help: education.ti.com
```

Displays the Product ID. Each Flash-based graphing calculator has a unique product ID, which you may need if you contact technical support. You can also use this 14 digit ID to register your calculator at education.ti.com, or identify your calculator in the event that it is lost or stolen.

Displaying the MEMORY MANAGEMENT/DELETE Menu

Mem Mgmt/Del displays the **MEMORY MANAGEMENT/DELETE** menu. The two lines at the top report the total amount of available RAM (**RAM FREE**) and Archive (**ARC FREE**) memory. By selecting menu items on this screen, you can see the amount of memory each variable type is using. This information can help you determine if you need to delete variables from memory to make room for new data, such as programs or Apps.

To check memory usage, follow these steps.

Memory and Variable Management

1. Press [2nd] [MEM] to display the **MEMORY** menu.

Note: The ↑ and ↓ in the top or bottom of the left column indicate that you can scroll up or down to view more variable types.

2. Select **2:Mem Mgmt/Del** to display the **MEMORY MANAGEMENT/DELETE** menu. The TI-84 Plus expresses memory quantities in bytes.

```
RAM FREE    24317
ARC FREE    1540K
1█All...
2:Real...
3:Complex...
4:List...
5:Matrix...
6↓Y-Vars...
```

```
7↑Prgm...
8:Pic...
9:GDB...
0:String...
A:Apps...
B↓AppVars...
```

```
C:Group...
```

3. Select variable types from the list to display memory usage.

    Notes: Real, List, Y-Vars, and **Prgm** variable types never reset to zero, even after memory is cleared.

    Apps are independent applications which are stored in Flash ROM. **AppVars** is a variable holder used to store variables created by Apps. You cannot edit or change variables in **AppVars** unless you do so through the application which created them.

To leave the **MEMORY MANAGEMENT/DELETE** menu, press either [2nd] [QUIT] or [CLEAR]. Both options display the home screen.

Deleting Items from Memory

Deleting an Item

To increase available memory by deleting the contents of any variable (real or complex number, list, matrix, **Y=** variable, program, Apps, AppVars, picture, graph database, or string), follow these steps.

1. Press [2nd] [MEM] to display the **MEMORY** menu.

2. Select **2:Mem Mgmt/Del** to display the **MEMORY MANAGEMENT/DELETE** menu.

3. Select the type of data you want to delete, or select **1:All** for a list of all variables of all types. A screen is displayed listing each variable of the type you selected and the number of bytes each variable is using.

    For example, if you select **4:List**, the **LIST** editor screen is displayed.

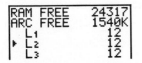

4. Press [▲] and [▼] to move the selection cursor (▸) next to the item you want to delete, and then press [DEL]. The variable is deleted from memory. You can delete individual variables one by one from this screen. No warning will be given to verify the deletion.

    Note: If you are deleting programs or Apps, you will receive a message asking you to confirm this delete action. Select **2:Yes** to continue.

    To leave any variable screen without deleting anything, press [2nd] [QUIT], which displays the home screen.

    You cannot delete some system variables, such as the last-answer variable **Ans** and the statistical variable **RegEQ**.

Clearing Entries and List Elements

Clear Entries

Clear Entries clears the contents of the **ENTRY** (last entry on home screen) storage area. To clear the **ENTRY** storage area, follow these steps.

1. Press [2nd] [MEM] to display the **MEMORY** menu.

2. Select **3:Clear Entries** to paste the instruction to the home screen.

3. Press [ENTER] to clear the **ENTRY** storage area.

```
Clear Entries
           Done
```

To cancel **Clear Entries**, press [CLEAR].

Note: If you select **3:Clear Entries** from within a program, the **Clear Entries** instruction is pasted to the program editor, and the **Entry** (last entry) is cleared when the program is executed.

ClrAllLists

ClrAllLists sets the dimension of each list in RAM to **0**.

To clear all elements from all lists, follow these steps.

1. Press [2nd] [MEM] to display the **MEMORY** menu.

2. Select **4:ClrAllLists** to paste the instruction to the home screen.

3. Press [ENTER] to set the dimension of each list in memory to **0**.

```
ClrAllLists
           Done
```

To cancel **ClrAllLists**, press [CLEAR].

ClrAllLists does not delete list names from memory, from the **LIST NAMES** menu, or from the stat list editor.

Note: If you select **4:ClrAllLists** from within a program, the **ClrAllLists** instruction is pasted to the program editor. The lists are cleared when the program is executed.

Archiving and UnArchiving Variables

Archiving and UnArchiving Variables

Archiving lets you store data, programs, or other variables to the user data archive (ARC) where they cannot be edited or deleted inadvertently. Archiving also allows you to free up RAM for variables that may require additional memory.

Archived variables cannot be edited or executed. They can only be seen and unarchived. For example, if you archive list **L1**, you will see that **L1** exists in memory but if you select it and paste the name **L1** to the home screen, you won't be able to see its contents or edit it.

Note: Not all variables may be archived. Not all archived variables may be unarchived. For example, system variables including r, t, x, y, and θ cannot be archived. Apps and Groups always exist in Flash ROM so there is no need to archive them. Groups cannot be unarchived. However, you can ungroup or delete them.

Variable Type	Names	Archive? (yes/no)	UnArchive? (yes/no)
Real numbers	**A, B, ... , Z**	yes	yes
Complex numbers	**A, B, ... , Z**	yes	yes
Matrices	**[A], [B], [C], ... , [J]**	yes	yes
Lists	**L1, L2, L3, L4, L5, L6,** and user-defined names	yes	yes
Programs		yes	yes
Functions	**Y1, Y2, . . . , Y9, Y0**	no	not applicable
Parametric equations	**X1T** and **Y1T, ... , X6T** and **Y6T**	no	not applicable
Polar functions	**r1, r2, r3, r4, r5, r6**	no	not applicable
Sequence functions	**u, v, w**	no	not applicable
Stat plots	**Plot1, Plot2, Plot3**	no	not applicable

Variable Type	Names	Archive? (yes/no)	UnArchive? (yes/no)
Graph databases	**GDB1, GDB2,...**	yes	yes
Graph pictures	**Pic1, Pic2, ... , Pic9, Pic0**	yes	yes
Strings	**Str1, Str2, . . . Str9, Str0**	yes	yes
Tables	**TblStart, Tb1, TblInput**	no	not applicable
Apps	Applications	see Note above	no
AppVars	Application variables	yes	yes
Groups		see Note above	no
Variables with reserved names	**minX, maxX, RegEQ,** and others	no	not applicable
System variables	**Xmin**, **Xmax**, and others	no	not applicable

Archiving and unarchiving can be done in two ways:

• Use the **5:Archive** or **6:UnArchive** commands from the **MEMORY** menu or **CATALOG**.

• Use a Memory Management editor screen.

Before archiving or unarchiving variables, particularly those with a large byte size (such as large programs) use the **MEMORY** menu to:

• Find the size of the variable.

• See if there is enough free space.

For:	Sizes must be such that:
Archive	Archive free size > variable size
UnArchive	RAM free size > variable size

Note: If there is not enough space, unarchive or delete variables as necessary. Be aware that when you unarchive a variable, not all the memory associated with that variable in user data archive will be released since the system keeps track of where the variable has been and where it is now in RAM.

Even if there appears to be enough free space, you may see a Garbage Collection message when you attempt to archive a variable. Depending on the usability of empty blocks in the user data archive, you may need to unarchive existing variables to create more free space.

To archive or unarchive a list variable (L1) using the Archive/UnArchive options from the **MEMORY** menu:

1. Press [2nd] [MEM] to display the **MEMORY** menu.

2. Select **5:Archive** or **6:UnArchive** to place the command in the **Home** screen.

3. Press [2nd] [L1] to place the **L1** variable in the **Home** screen.

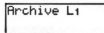

4. Press [ENTER] to complete the archive process.

```
Archive L1
            Done
```

Note: An asterisk will be displayed to the left of the Archived variable name to indicate it is archived.

To archive or unarchive a list variable (L1) using a Memory Management editor:

1. Press [2nd] [MEM] to display the **MEMORY** menu.

```
MEMORY
1:About
2:Mem Mgmt/Del…
3:Clear Entries
4:ClrAllLists
5:Archive
6:UnArchive
7↓Reset…
```

2. Select **2:Mem Mgmt/Del** to display the **MEMORY MANAGEMENT/DELETE** menu.

```
RAM FREE    23896
ARC FREE   868260
1█All…
2:Real…
3:Complex…
4:List…
5:Matrix…
6↓Y-Vars…
```

3. Select **4:List** to display the **LIST** menu.

```
RAM FREE    23896
ARC FREE   868260
► L1          12
  L2          12
  L3          12
  L4          12
  L5          12
  L6          12
```

4. Press [ENTER] to archive **L1**. An asterisk will appear to the left of **L1** to indicate it is an archived variable. To unarchive a variable in this screen, put the cursor next to the archived variable and press [ENTER]. The asterisk will disappear.

```
RAM FREE    23894
ARC FREE   868235
►*L1          12
  L2          12
  L3          12
  L4          12
  L5          12
  L6          12
```

5. Press [2nd] [QUIT] to leave the **LIST** menu.

Note: You can access an archived variable for the purpose of linking, deleting, or unarchiving it, but you cannot edit it.

Resetting the TI-84 Plus

RAM ARCHIVE ALL Menu

Reset displays the **RAM ARCHIVE ALL** menu. This menu gives you the option of resetting all memory (including default settings) or resetting selected portions of memory while preserving other data stored in memory, such as programs and **Y=** functions. For instance, you can choose to reset all of RAM or just restore the default settings. Be aware that if you choose to reset RAM, all data and programs in RAM will be erased. For archive memory, you can reset variables (Vars), applications (Apps), or both of these. Be aware that if you choose to reset Vars, all data and programs in archive memory will be erased. If you choose to reset Apps, all applications in archive memory will be erased.

When you reset defaults on the TI-84 Plus, all defaults in RAM are restored to the factory settings. Stored data and programs are not changed.

These are some examples of TI-84 Plus defaults that are restored by resetting the defaults.

* Mode settings such as **Normal** (notation); **Func** (graphing); **Real** (numbers); and **Full** (screen)

* **Y=** functions off

* Window variable values such as **Xmin=‑10, Xmax=10, Xscl=1, Yscl=1,** and **Xres=1**

* **STAT PLOTS** off

* Format settings such as **CoordOn** (graphing coordinates on); **AxesOn**; and **ExprOn** (expression on)

* **rand** seed value to 0

Displaying the RAM ARCHIVE ALL Menu

To display the **RAM ARCHIVE ALL** menu on the TI-84 Plus, follow these steps.

1. Press [2nd] [MEM] to display the **MEMORY** menu.

2. Select **7:Reset** to display the **RAM ARCHIVE ALL** menu.

```
RAM ARCHIVE ALL
1:All RAM…
2:Defaults…
```

Resetting RAM Memory

Resetting all RAM restores RAM system variables to factory settings and deletes all nonsystem variables and all programs. Resetting RAM defaults restores all system variables to default settings without deleting variables and programs in RAM. Resetting all RAM or resetting defaults does not affect variables and applications in user data archive.

Note: Before you reset all RAM memory, consider restoring sufficient available memory by deleting only selected data.

To reset all **RAM** memory or **RAM** defaults on the TI-84 Plus, follow these steps.

1. From the **RAM ARCHIVE ALL** menu, select **1:All RAM** to display the **RESET RAM** menu or **2:Defaults** to display the **RESET DEFAULTS** menu.

2. If you are resetting RAM, read the message below the **RESET RAM** menu.

    *   To cancel the reset and return to the **HOME** screen, press [ENTER].

    *   To erase RAM memory or reset defaults, select **2:Reset**. Depending on your choice, the message **RAM cleared** or **Defaults set** is displayed on the home screen.

Resetting Archive Memory

When resetting archive memory on the TI-84 Plus, you can choose to delete from user data archive all variables, all applications, or both variables and applications.

To reset all or part of user data archive memory, follow these steps.

1. From the **RAM ARCHIVE ALL** menu, press [▶] to display the **ARCHIVE** menu.

```
RAM ARCHIVE ALL
1:Vars…
2:Apps…
3:Both…
```

2. Select one of the following:

1:Vars to display the **RESET ARC VARS** menu.

2:Apps to display the **RESET ARC APPS** menu.

3:Both to display the **RESET ARC BOTH** menu.

```
RESET ARC BOTH
1▪No
2:Reset

Resetting Both
erases all data,
programs & Apps
from Archive.
```

3. Read the message below the menu.

    •   To cancel the reset and return to the **HOME** screen, press ENTER.

    •   To continue with the reset, select **2:Reset**. A message indicating the type of archive memory cleared will be displayed on the **HOME** screen.

Resetting All Memory

When resetting all memory on the TI-84 Plus, RAM and user data archive memory is restored to factory settings. All nonsystem variables, applications, and programs are deleted. All system variables are reset to default settings.

Before you reset all memory, consider restoring sufficient available memory by deleting only selected data.

To reset all memory on the TI-84 Plus, follow these steps.

1. From the **RAM ARCHIVE ALL** menu, press ▶▶ to display the **ALL** menu.

```
RAM ARCHIVE ALL
1:All Memory..
```

2. Select **1:All Memory** to display the **RESET MEMORY** menu.

```
RESET MEMORY
1:No
2:Reset
Resetting ALL
will delete all
data, programs &
Apps from RAM &
Archive.
```

3. Read the message below the **RESET MEMORY** menu.

   • To cancel the reset and return to the **HOME** screen, press [ENTER].

   • To continue with the reset, select **2:Reset**. The message **MEM cleared** is displayed on the **HOME** screen.

When you clear memory, the contrast sometimes changes. If the screen is faded or blank, adjust the contrast by pressing [2nd] [▲] or [▼].

Grouping and Ungrouping Variables

Grouping Variables

Grouping allows you to make a copy of two or more variables residing in RAM and then store them as a group in user data archive. The variables in RAM are not erased. The variables must exist in RAM before they can be grouped. In other words, archived data cannot be included in a group. Once grouped, the variables can be deleted from RAM to open memory. When the variables are needed later, they can be ungrouped for use.

To create a group of variables:

1. Press [2nd] [MEM] to display the **MEMORY** menu.

2. Select **8:Group** to display **GROUP UNGROUP** menu.

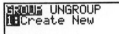

3. Press [ENTER] to display the **GROUP** menu.

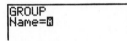

4. Enter a name for the new group and press [ENTER].

    Note: A group name can be one to eight characters long. The first character must be a letter from A to Z or θ. The second through eighth characters can be letters, numbers, or θ.

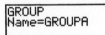

5. Select the type of data you want to group. You can select **1:All+** which shows all variables of all types available and selected. You can also select **1:All-** which shows all variables of all types available but not selected. A screen is displayed listing each variable of the type you selected.

For example, suppose some variables have been created in RAM, and selecting **1:All-** displays the following screen.

```
SELECT  Done
►  PROGRAM1  PRGM
   PROGRAM2  PRGM
   GDB1      GDB
   L₁        LIST
   L₂        LIST
   L₃        LIST
   L₄        LIST
```

6. Press ⏶ and ⏷ to move the selection cursor (►) next to the first item you want to copy into a group, and then press ENTER. A small square will remain to the left of all variables selected for grouping.

```
SELECT  Done
   PROGRAM1  PRGM
■  PROGRAM2  PRGM
■  GDB1      GDB
■  L₁        LIST
   L₂        LIST
♦  L₃        LIST
   L₄        LIST
```

Repeat the selection process until all variables for the new group are selected and then press ▶ to display the **DONE** menu.

```
SELECT  DONE
1■Done
```

7. Press ENTER to complete the grouping process.

```
Copying
Variables to
Group:
GROUPA
              Done
```

Note: You can only group variables in RAM. You cannot group some system variables, such as the last-answer variable **Ans** and the statistical variable **RegEQ**.

Ungrouping Variables

Ungrouping allows you to make a copy of variables in a group stored in user data archive and place them ungrouped in **RAM**.

DuplicateName Menu

During the ungrouping action, if a duplicate variable name is detected in **RAM**, the **DUPLICATE NAME** menu is displayed.

DuplicateName	
1: Rename	Prompts to rename receiving variable.
2: Overwrite	Overwrites data in receiving duplicate variable.
3: Overwrite All	Overwrites data in all receiving duplicate variables.
4: Omit	Skips ungrouping of sending variable.
5: Quit	Stops ungrouping at duplicate variable.

Notes about Menu Items:

- When you select **1:Rename**, the **Name=** prompt is displayed, and alpha-lock is on. Enter a new variable name, and then press [ENTER]. Ungrouping resumes.

- When you select **2:Overwrite**, the unit overwrites the data of the duplicate variable name found in RAM. Ungrouping resumes.

- When you select **3: Overwrite All**, the unit overwrites the data of all duplicate variable names found in RAM. Ungrouping resumes.

- When you select **4:Omit**, the unit does not ungroup the variable in conflict with the duplicated variable name found in RAM. Ungrouping resumes with the next item.

- When you select **5:Quit**, ungrouping stops, and no further changes are made.

To ungroup a group of variables:

1. Press [2nd] [MEM] to display the **MEMORY** menu.

```
MEMORY
2↑Mem Mgmt/Del…
3:Clear Entries
4:ClrAllLists
5:Archive
6:UnArchive
7:Reset…
8█Group…
```

2. Select **8:Group** to display the **GROUP UNGROUP** menu.

3. Press [▶] to display the **UNGROUP** menu.

4. Press ▲ and ▼ to move the selection cursor (▶) next to the group variable you want to ungroup, and then press [ENTER].

```
Ungrouping:
GROUP1
                Done
```

The ungroup action is completed.

Note: Ungrouping does not remove the group from user data archive. You must delete the group in user data archive to remove it.

Garbage Collection

Garbage Collection Message

If you use the user data archive extensively, you may see a **Garbage Collect?** message. This occurs if you try to archive a variable when there is not enough free contiguous archive memory.

The **Garbage Collect?** message lets you know an archive will take longer than usual. It also alerts you that the archive will fail if there is not enough memory.

The message can also alert you when a program is caught in a loop that repetitively fills the user data archive. Select **No** to cancel the garbage collection process, and then find and correct the errors in your program.

When YES is selected, the TI-84 Plus will attempt to rearrange the archived variables to make additional room.

Responding to the Garbage Collection Message

- To cancel, select **1:No**.

- If you select **1:No**, the message **ERR:ARCHIVE FULL** will be displayed.

- To continue archiving, select **2:Yes**.

- If you select **2:Yes**, the process message **Garbage Collecting...** or **Defragmenting...** will be displayed.

Note: The process message **Defragmenting...** is displayed whenever an application marked for deletion is encountered. Garbage collection may take up to 20 minutes, depending on how much of archive memory has been used to store variables.

After garbage collection, depending on how much additional space is freed, the variable may or may not be archived. If not, you can unarchive some variables and try again.

Why Is Garbage Collection Necessary?

The user data archive is divided into sectors. When you first begin archiving, variables are stored consecutively in sector 1. This continues to the end of the sector.

An archived variable is stored in a continuous block within a single sector. Unlike an application stored in user data archive, an archived variable cannot cross a sector boundary. If there is not enough space left in the sector, the next variable is stored at the beginning of the next sector. Typically, this leaves an empty block at the end of the previous sector.

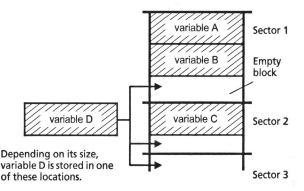

Each variable that you archive is stored in the first empty block large enough to hold it.

This process continues to the end of the last sector. Depending on the size of individual variables, the empty blocks may account for a significant amount of space. Garbage collection occurs when the variable you are archiving is larger than any empty block.

How Unarchiving a Variable Affects the Process

When you unarchive a variable, it is copied to RAM but it is not actually deleted from user data archive memory. Unarchived variables are "marked for deletion," meaning they will be deleted during the next garbage collection.

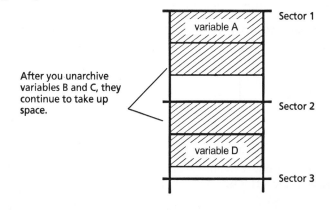

If the MEMORY Screen Shows Enough Free Space

Even if the **MEMORY** screen shows enough free space to archive a variable or store an application, you may still get a **Garbage Collect?** message or an **ERR: ARCHIVE FULL** message.

When you unarchive a variable, the **Archive free** amount increases immediately, but the space is not actually available until after the next garbage collection.

If the **Archive free** amount shows enough available space for your variable, there probably will be enough space to archive it after garbage collection (depending on the usability of any empty blocks).

The Garbage Collection Process

The garbage collection process:

- Deletes unarchived variables from the user data archive.

- Rearranges the remaining variables into consecutive blocks.

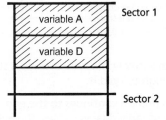

Note: Power loss during garbage collection may cause all memory (RAM and Archive) to be deleted.

Using the GarbageCollect Command

You can reduce the number of automatic garbage collections by periodically optimizing memory. This is done by using the **GarbageCollect** command.

To use the **GarbageCollect** command, follow these steps.

1. From the **HOME** screen, press [2nd] [CATALOG] to display the **CATALOG**.

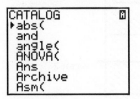

2. Press [▼] or [▲] to scroll the **CATALOG** until the selection cursor points to the **GarbageCollect** command or press G to skip to the commands starting with the letter G.

3. Press ENTER to paste the command to the **HOME** screen.
4. Press ENTER to display the **Garbage Collect?** message.
5. Select **2:Yes** to begin garbage collection.

ERR:ARCHIVE FULL Message

Even if the **MEMORY** screen shows enough free space to archive a variable or store an application, you may still get an **ERR: ARCHIVE FULL** message.

```
ERR:ARCHIVE FULL
1∎Quit

Largest single…
 Variable=  9662
 App     =     0
```

An **ERR:ARCHIVE FULL** message may be displayed:

*   When there is insufficient space to archive a variable within a continuous block and within a single sector.

*   When there is insufficient space to store an application within a continuous block of memory.

When the message is displayed, it will indicate the largest single space of memory available for storing a variable and an application.

To resolve the problem, use the **GarbageCollect** command to optimize memory. If memory is still insufficient, you must delete variables or applications to increase space.

4

Communication Link

Getting Started: Sending Variables

Getting Started is a fast-paced introduction. Read the chapter for details.

Create and store a variable and a matrix, and then transfer them to another TI-84 Plus.

1. On the home screen of the sending unit, press **5** ⌷ **5** STO▸ ALPHA **Q**. Press ENTER to store 5.5 to **Q**.

2. Press 2nd [[ ] 2nd [[ ] **1** ⌷ **2** 2nd [ ]] 2nd [[ ] **3** ⌷ **4** 2nd [ ]] 2nd [ ]] STO▸ 2nd [MATRIX] **1**. Press ENTER to store the matrix to [A].

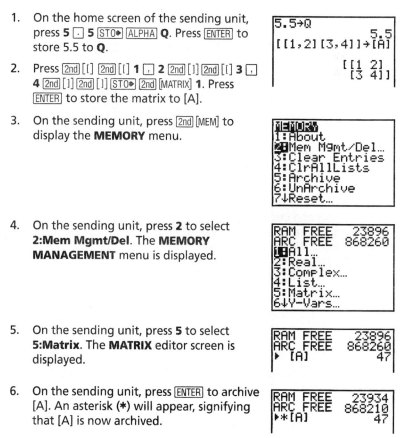

3. On the sending unit, press 2nd [MEM] to display the **MEMORY** menu.

4. On the sending unit, press **2** to select **2:Mem Mgmt/Del**. The **MEMORY MANAGEMENT** menu is displayed.

5. On the sending unit, press **5** to select **5:Matrix**. The **MATRIX** editor screen is displayed.

6. On the sending unit, press ENTER to archive [A]. An asterisk (✱) will appear, signifying that [A] is now archived.

7. Connect the graphing calculators with the USB unit-to-unit cable. Push both ends in firmly.

8. On the receiving unit, press [2nd] [LINK] [▶] to display the **RECEIVE** menu. Press **1** to select **1:Receive**. The message **Waiting...** is displayed and the busy indicator is on.

9. On the sending unit, press [2nd] [LINK] to display the **SEND** menu.

10. Press **2** to select **2:All–**. The **All– SELECT** screen is displayed.

11. Press [▾] until the selection cursor (▶) is next to [A] **MATRX**. Press [ENTER].

12. Press [▾] until the selection cursor is next to **Q REAL**. Press [ENTER]. A square dot next to [A] and **Q** indicates that each is selected to send.

13. On the sending unit, press [▶] to display the **TRANSMIT** menu.

14. On the sending unit, press **1** to select **1:Transmit** and begin transmission. The receiving unit displays the message **Receiving....**When the items are transmitted, both units display the name and type of each transmitted variable.

TI-84 Plus LINK

This chapter describes how to communicate with compatible TI units. The TI-84 Plus has a USB port to connect and communicate with another TI-84 Plus or TI-84 Plus Silver Edition. A USB unit-to-unit cable is included with the TI-84 Plus.

The TI-84 Plus also has an I/O port using a I/O unit-to-unit cable to communicate with:

- TI-83 Plus Silver Edition
- TI-82
- TI-83 Plus
- TI-73
- TI-83
- CBL 2™ or a CBR™

Connecting Two Graphing Calculators with a USB Unit-to-Unit Cable or an I/O Unit-to-Unit Cable

USB Unit-to-Unit Cable

The TI-84 Plus USB link port is located at the top right edge of the graphing calculator.

1. Firmly insert either end of the USB unit-to-unit cable into the USB port.

2. Insert the other end of the cable into the other graphing calculator's USB port.

I/O Unit-to-Unit Cable

The TI-84 Plus I/O link port is located at the top left edge of the graphing calculator.

1. Firmly insert either end of the I/O unit-to-unit cable into the port.

2. Insert the other end of the cable into the other graphing calculator's I/O port.

TI-84 Plus to a TI-83 Plus using I/O Unit-to-Unit Cable

The TI-84 Plus I/O link port is located at the top left edge of the graphing calculator. The TI-83 Plus I/O link port is located at the bottom edge of the graphing calculator.

1. Firmly insert either end of the I/O unit-to-unit cable into the port.

2. Insert the other end of the cable into the other graphing calculator's I/O port.

Linking to the CBL/CBR System

The CBL 2™ and the CBR™ are optional accessories that also connect to a TI-84 Plus with the I/O unit-to-unit cable. With a CBL 2 or CBR and a TI-84 Plus, you can collect and analyze real-world data.

Linking to a Computer

With TI Connect™ software and the USB computer cable that is included with your TI-84 Plus, you can link the graphing calculator to a personal computer.

Selecting Items to Send

LINK SEND Menu

To display the **LINK SEND** menu, press [2nd] [LINK].

SEND   RECEIVE

1: All+...	Displays all items as selected, including RAM and Flash applications.
2: All-...	Displays all items as deselected.
3: Prgm...	Displays all program names.
4: List...	Displays all list names.
5: Lists to TI82...	Displays list names **L1** through **L6**.
6: GDB...	Displays all graph databases.
7: Pic...	Displays all picture data types.
8: Matrix...	Displays all matrix data types.
9: Real...	Displays all real variables.
0: Complex...	Displays all complex variables.
A: Y-Vars...	Displays all **Y=** variables.
B: String...	Displays all string variables.
C: Apps...	Displays all software applications.
D: AppVars...	Displays all software application variables.
E: Group...	Displays all grouped variables.
F: SendId	Sends the Calculator ID number immediately. (You do not need to select **SEND**.)
G: SendOS	Sends operating system updates to another TI-84 Plus Silver Edition or TI-84 Plus. You can not send the operating system to the TI-83 Plus product family.
H: Back Up...	Selects all RAM and mode settings (no Flash applications or archived items) for backup to another TI-84 Plus, TI-84 Plus Silver Edition, TI-83 Plus Silver Edition, or to a TI-83 Plus.

When you select an item on the **LINK SEND** menu, the corresponding **SELECT** screen is displayed.

Note: Each **SELECT** screen, except **All+...**, is initially displayed with nothing pre-selected. **All+...** is displayed with everything pre-selected.

To select items to send:

1. Press [2nd] [LINK] on the sending unit to display the **LINK SEND** menu.

2. Select the menu item that describes the data type to send. The corresponding **SELECT** screen is displayed.

3. Press ⊡ and ⊡ to move the selection cursor (▶) to an item you want to select or deselect.

4. Press [ENTER] to select or deselect the item. Selected names are marked with a ▪.

```
SELECT TRANSMIT
▪ *PROGRAM1  PRGM
   PROGRAM2  PRGM
▪ *GDB1      GDB
▪  L₁        LIST
▪ *L₂        LIST
▪ *L₃        LIST
▶  L₄        LIST
```

Note: An asterisk (*) to the left of an item indicates the item is archived.

5. Repeat steps 3 and 4 to select or deselect additional items.

Sending the Selected Items

After you have selected items to send on the sending unit and set the receiving unit to receive, follow these steps to transmit the items. To set the receiving unit, see Receiving Items.

1. Press ▶ on the sending unit to display the **TRANSMIT** menu.

```
SELECT TRANSMIT
1▪Transmit
```

2. Confirm that **Waiting...** is displayed on the receiving unit, which indicates it is set to receive.

3. Press [ENTER] to select **1:Transmit**. The name and type of each item are displayed line-by-line on the sending unit as the item is queued for transmission, and then on the receiving unit as each item is accepted.

Note: Items sent from the RAM of the sending unit are transmitted to the RAM of the receiving unit. Items sent from user data archive (flash) of the sending unit are transmitted to user data archive (flash) of the receiving unit.

After all selected items have been transmitted, the message **Done** is displayed on both calculators. Press ⬆ and ⬇ to scroll through the names.

Sending to a TI-84 Plus Silver Edition or TI-84 Plus

You can transfer variables (all types), programs, and Flash applications to another TI-84 Plus Silver Edition or TI-84 Plus. You can also backup the RAM memory of one unit to another.

Note: Keep in mind that the TI-84 Plus has less Flash memory than the TI-84 Plus Silver Edition.

- Variables stored in RAM on the sending TI-84 Plus Silver Edition will be sent to the RAM of the receiving TI-84 Plus Silver Edition or TI-84 Plus.

- Variables and applications stored in the user data archive of the sending TI-84 Plus Silver Edition will be sent to the user data archive of the receiving TI-84 Plus Silver Edition or TI-84 Plus.

After sending or receiving data, you can repeat the same transmission to additional TI-84 Plus Silver Edition or TI-84 Plus units—from either the sending unit or the receiving unit—without having to reselect data to send. The current items remain selected. However, you cannot repeat transmission if you selected **All+** or **All-**.

To send data to an additional TI-84 Plus Silver Edition or a TI-84 Plus:

1. Use a USB unit-to-unit cable to link two units together.

2. On the sending unit press [2nd] [LINK] and select a data type and items to **SEND**.

3. Press ▶ on the sending unit to display the **TRANSMIT** menu.

4. On the other unit, press [2nd] [LINK] ▶ to display the **RECEIVE** menu.

5. Press [ENTER] on the receiving unit.

6. Press [ENTER] on the sending unit. A copy of the selected item(s) is sent to the receiving unit.

7. Disconnect the link cable only from the receiving unit and connect it to another unit.

8. Press [2nd] [LINK] on the sending unit.

9. Select only the data type. For example, if the unit just sent a list, select **4:LIST**.

   Note: The item(s) you want to send are pre-selected from the last transmission. Do not select or deselect any items. If you select or

---

deselect an item, all selections or deselections from the last transmission are cleared.

10. Press ▶ on the sending unit to display the **TRANSMIT** menu.

11. On the new receiving unit, press [2nd] [LINK] ▶ to display the **RECEIVE** menu.

12. Press [ENTER] on the receiving unit.

13. Press [ENTER] on the sending unit. A copy of the selected item(s) is sent to the receiving unit.

14. Repeat steps 7 through 13 until the items are sent to all additional units.

Sending to a TI-83 Plus or TI-83 Plus Silver Edition

You can send all variables from a TI-84 Plus to a TI-83 Plus or TI-83 Plus Silver Edition *except* Flash applications with new features, or programs with new features in them.

If archived variables on the TI-84 Plus are variable types recognized and used on the TI-83 Plus or TI-83 Plus Silver Edition, you can send these variables to the TI-83 Plus or TI-83 Plus Silver Edition. They will be automatically sent to the RAM of the TI-83 Plus or TI-83 Plus Silver Edition during the transfer process. It will send to archive if the item is from archive.

To send data to a TI-83 Plus or TI-83 Plus Silver Edition:

1. Use an I/O unit-to-unit cable to link the two units together.

2. Set the TI-83 Plus or TI-83 Plus Silver Edition to receive.

3. Press [2nd] [LINK] on the sending TI-84 Plus to display the **LINK SEND** menu.

4. Select the menu of the items you want to transmit.

5. Press ▶ on the sending TI-84 Plus to display the **LINK TRANSMIT** menu.

6. Confirm that the receiving unit is set to receive.

7. Press [ENTER] on the sending TI-84 Plus to select **1:Transmit** and begin transmitting.

Receiving Items

LINK RECEIVE Menu

To display the **LINK RECEIVE** menu, press [2nd] [LINK] [▶].

SEND   RECEIVE

1: Receive   Sets unit to receive data transmission.

Receiving Unit

When you select **1:Receive** from the **LINK RECEIVE** menu on the receiving unit, the message **Waiting...** and the busy indicator are displayed. The receiving unit is ready to receive transmitted items. To exit the receive mode without receiving items, press [ON], and then select **1:Quit** from the **Error in Xmit** menu.

When transmission is complete, the unit exits the receive mode. You can select **1:Receive** again to receive more items. The receiving unit then displays a list of items received. Press [2nd] [QUIT] to exit the receive mode.

DuplicateName Menu

During transmission, if a variable name is duplicated, the **DuplicateName** menu is displayed on the receiving unit.

DuplicateName

1: Rename	Prompts to rename receiving variable.
2: Overwrite	Overwrites data in receiving variable.
3: Omit	Skips transmission of sending variable.
4: Quit	Stops transmission at duplicate variable.

When you select **1:Rename**, the **Name=** prompt is displayed, and alpha-lock is on. Enter a new variable name, and then press [ENTER]. Transmission resumes.

When you select **2:Overwrite**, the sending unit's data overwrites the existing data stored on the receiving unit. Transmission resumes.

When you select **3:Omit**, the sending unit does not send the data in the duplicated variable name. Transmission resumes with the next item.

When you select **4:Quit**, transmission stops, and the receiving unit exits receive mode.

Receiving from a TI-84 Plus Silver Edition or TI-84 Plus

The TI-84 Plus Silver Edition and the TI-84 Plus are totally compatible. Keep in mind, however that the TI-84 Plus has less Flash memory than a TI-84 Plus Silver Edition.

You cannot send memory backups between the TI-84 Plus product family and the TI-83 Plus product family.

Receiving from a TI-83 Plus Silver Edition or TI-83 Plus

The TI-84 Plus product family and the TI-83 Plus product family are compatible with a few exceptions.

Receiving from a TI-83

You can transfer all variables and programs from a TI-83 to a TI-84 Plus if they fit in the RAM of the TI-84 Plus. The RAM of the TI-84 Plus is slightly less than the RAM of the TI-83.

Backing Up RAM Memory

Warning: H:Back Up overwrites the RAM memory and mode settings in the receiving unit. All information in the RAM memory of the receiving unit is lost.

Note: Archived items on the receiving unit are not overwritten.

You can backup the contents of RAM memory and mode settings (no Flash applications or archived items) to another TI-84 Plus Silver Edition. You can also backup RAM memory and mode settings to a TI-84 Plus.

To perform a RAM memory backup:

1. Use a USB unit-to-unit cable to link two TI-84 Plus units, or a TI-84 Plus and a TI-84 Plus Silver Edition together.

2. On the sending unit press [2nd] [LINK] and select **H:Back Up**. The **MEMORYBACKUP** screen displays.

3. On the receiving unit, press [2nd] [LINK] [▶] to display the **RECEIVE** menu.

4. Press [ENTER] on the receiving unit.

5. Press [ENTER] on the sending unit. A **WARNING — Backup** message displays on the receiving unit.

6. Press [ENTER] on the receiving unit to continue the backup.
   — or —
   Press **2:Quit** on the receiving unit to cancel the backup and return to the **LINK SEND** menu

   Note: If a transmission error is returned during a backup, the receiving unit is reset.

Memory Backup Complete

When the backup is complete, both the sending graphing calculator and receiving graphing calculator display a confirmation screen.

Error Conditions

A transmission error occurs after one or two seconds if:

- A cable is not attached to the sending unit.
- A cable is not attached to the receiving unit.

  Note: If the cable is attached, push it in firmly and try again.

- The receiving unit is not set to receive transmission.
- You attempt a backup between a TI-73, TI-82, TI-83, TI-83 Plus, TI-83 Plus Silver Edition
- You attempt a data transfer from a TI-84 Plus to a TI-83 Plus, TI-83 Plus Silver Edition, TI-83, TI-82, or TI-73 with variables or features not recognized by the TI-83 Plus, TI-83 Plus Silver Edition, TI-83, TI-82, or TI-73.

  New variable types and features not recognized by the TI-83, TI-83 Plus, TI-82, or TI-73 include applications, application variables, grouped variables, new variable types, or programs with new features in them such as **Archive, UnArchive, SendID, SendOS, Asm(, AsmComp(, AsmPrgm, checkTmr(, ClockOff, ClockOn, dayOfWk(, getDate, getDtFmt, getDtStr(, getTime, getTmFmt, getTmStr, isClockOn, setDate(, setDtFmt(, setTime(, setTmFmt(, startTmr,** and **timeCnv.**

- You attempt a data transfer from a TI-84 Plus to a TI-82 with data other than real lists **L1** through **L6** or without using menu item **5:Lists to TI82.**
- You attempt a data transfer from a TI-84 Plus to a TI-73 with data other than real numbers, pics, real lists **L1** through **L6** or named lists with θ as part of the name.
- Although a transmission error does not occur, these two conditions may prevent successful transmission.
- You try to use **Get(** with a graphing calculator instead of a CBL 2™ or CBR™.
- You try to use **GetCalc(** with a TI-83 instead of a TI-84 Plus or TI-84 Plus Silver Edition.

Insufficient Memory in Receiving Unit

- During transmission, if the receiving unit does not have sufficient memory to receive an item, the **Memory Full** menu is displayed on the receiving unit.
- To skip this item for the current transmission, select **1:Omit.** Transmission resumes with the next item.
- To cancel the transmission and exit receive mode, select **2:Quit.**

A

Appendix A: Functions and Instructions

Functions return a value, list, or matrix. You can use functions in an expression. Instructions initiate an action. Some functions and instructions have arguments. Optional arguments and accompanying commas are enclosed in brackets ([ ]). For details about an item, including argument descriptions and restrictions, turn to the page listed on the right side of the table.

From the **CATALOG**, you can paste any function or instruction to the home screen or to a command line in the program editor. However, some functions and instructions are not valid on the home screen. The items in this table appear in the same order as they appear in the **CATALOG**.

† indicates either keystrokes that are valid in the program editor only or ones that paste certain instructions when you are in the program editor. Some keystrokes display menus that are available only in the program editor. Others paste mode, format, or table-set instructions only when you are in the program editor.

Function or Instruction/Arguments	Result	Key or Keys/Menu or Screen/Item
abs(_value_**)**	Returns the absolute value of a real number, expression, list, or matrix.	MATH **NUM** **1:abs(**
abs(_complex value_**)**	Returns the magnitude of a complex number or list.	MATH **CPX** **5:abs(**
valueA **and** _valueB_	Returns 1 if both _valueA_ and _valueB_ are ≠ 0. _valueA_ and _valueB_ can be real numbers, expressions, or lists.	[2nd] [TEST] **LOGIC** **1:and**
angle(_value_**)**	Returns the polar angle of a complex number or list of complex numbers.	MATH **CPX** **4:angle(**

Function or Instruction/Arguments	Result	Key or Keys/Menu or Screen/Item
ANOVA(list1,list2 [,list3,...,list20]**)**	Performs a one-way analysis of variance for comparing the means of two to 20 populations.	STAT **TESTS** **H:ANOVA(**
Ans	Returns the last answer.	2nd [ANS]
Archive	Moves the specified variables from RAM to the user data archive memory.	2nd [MEM] **5:Archive**
Asm(assemblyprgmname**)**	Executes an assembly language program.	2nd [CATALOG] **Asm(**
AsmComp(prgmASM1, prgmASM2**)**	Compiles an assembly language program written in ASCII and stores the hex version.	2nd [CATALOG] **AsmComp(**
AsmPrgm	Must be used as the first line of an assembly language program.	2nd [CATALOG] **AsmPrgm**
augment(matrixA, matrixB**)**	Returns a matrix, which is matrixB appended to matrixA as new columns.	2nd [MATRIX] **MATH** **7:augment(**
augment(listA,listB**)**	Returns a list, which is listB concatenated to the end of listA.	2nd [LIST] **OPS** **9:augment(**
AxesOff	Turns off the graph axes.	† 2nd [FORMAT] **AxesOff**
AxesOn	Turns on the graph axes.	† 2nd [FORMAT] **AxesOn**
a+bi	Sets the mode to rectangular complex number mode (a+bi).	† MODE **a+b**i

Function or Instruction/Arguments	Result	Key or Keys/Menu or Screen/Item
bal(_npmt_[,_roundvalue_]**)**	Computes the balance at _npmt_ for an amortization schedule using stored values for **PV**, I%, and **PMT** and rounds the computation to _roundvalue_.	[APPS] **1:Finance** **CALC** **9:bal(**
binomcdf(_numtrials,p_ [,_x_]**)**	Computes a cumulative probability at _x_ for the discrete binomial distribution with the specified _numtrials_ and probability _p_ of success on each trial.	[2nd] [DISTR] **DISTR** **B:binomcdf(**
binompdf(_numtrials,p_ [,_x_]**)**	Computes a probability at _x_ for the discrete binomial distribution with the specified _numtrials_ and probability _p_ of success on each trial.	[2nd] [DISTR] **DISTR** **A:binompdf(**
χ^2**cdf(**_lowerbound, upperbound,df_**)**	Computes the χ^2 distribution probability between _lowerbound_ and _upperbound_ for the specified degrees of freedom _df_.	[2nd] [DISTR] **DISTR** **8:χ^2cdf(**
χ^2**pdf(**_x,df_**)**	Computes the probability density function (pdf) for the χ^2 distribution at a specified _x_ value for the specified degrees of freedom _df_.	[2nd] [DISTR] **DISTR** **7:χ^2pdf(**
χ^2**-Test(**_observedmatrix, expectedmatrix_ [,_drawflag_]**)**	Performs a chi-square test. _drawflag_=**1** draws results; _drawflag_=**0** calculates results.	† [STAT] **TESTS** **C:χ^2-Test(**

Function or Instruction/Arguments	Result	Key or Keys/Menu or Screen/Item
χ^2GOF-**Test(***observedlist, expectedlist,df***)**	Performs a test to confirm that sample data is from a population that conforms to a specified distribution.	† [STAT] **TESTS** **D:**χ^2GOF-**Test(**
checkTmr(*starttime***)**	Returns the number of seconds since you used **startTmr** to start the timer. The *starttime* is the value displayed by **startTmr.**	[2nd] [CATALOG] **checkTmr(**
Circle(*X,Y,radius***)**	Draws a circle with center (*X,Y*) and *radius*.	[2nd] [DRAW] **DRAW** **9:Circle(**
Clear Entries	Clears the contents of the Last Entry storage area.	[2nd] [MEM] **MEMORY** **3:Clear Entries**
ClockOff	Turns off the clock display in the mode screen.	[2nd] [CATALOG] **ClockOff**
ClockOn	Turns on the clock display in the mode screen.	[2nd] [CATALOG] **ClockOn**
ClrAllLists	Sets to **0** the dimension of all lists in memory.	[2nd] [MEM] **MEMORY** **4:ClrAllLists**
ClrDraw	Clears all drawn elements from a graph or drawing.	[2nd] [DRAW] **DRAW** **1:ClrDraw**
ClrHome	Clears the home screen.	† [PRGM] **I/O** **8:ClrHome**
ClrList *listname1* **[***,listname2, ..., listname n***]**	Sets to **0** the dimension of one or more *listnames*.	[STAT] **EDIT** **4:ClrList**
ClrTable	Clears all values from the table.	† [PRGM] **I/O** **9:ClrTable**

Function or Instruction/Arguments	Result	Key or Keys/Menu or Screen/Item
conj(*value*)	Returns the complex conjugate of a complex number or list of complex numbers.	MATH **CPX** **1:conj(**
Connected	Sets connected plotting mode; resets all **Y=** editor graph-style settings to \ .	† MODE **Connected**
CoordOff	Turns off cursor coordinate value display.	† 2nd [FORMAT] **CoordOff**
CoordOn	Turns on cursor coordinate value display.	† 2nd [FORMAT] **CoordOn**
cos(*value*)	Returns cosine of a real number, expression, or list.	COS
cos^{-1}(*value*)	Returns arccosine of a real number, expression, or list.	2nd [COS⁻¹]
cosh(*value*)	Returns hyperbolic cosine of a real number, expression, or list.	2nd [CATALOG] **cosh(**
cosh^{-1} (*value*)	Returns hyperbolic arccosine of a real number, expression, or list.	2nd [CATALOG] **cosh**$^{-1}$**(**
CubicReg [*Xlistname, Ylistname,freqlist, regequ*]	Fits a cubic regression model to *Xlistname* and *Ylistname* with frequency *freqlist*, and stores the regression equation to *regequ*.	STAT **CALC** **6:CubicReg**
cumSum(*list*)	Returns a list of the cumulative sums of the elements in *list*, starting with the first element.	2nd [LIST] **OPS** **6:cumSum(**

Function or Instruction/Arguments	Result	Key or Keys/Menu or Screen/Item
cumSum(*matrix***)**	Returns a matrix of the cumulative sums of *matrix* elements. Each element in the returned matrix is a cumulative sum of a *matrix* column from top to bottom.	[2nd] [MATRIX] **MATH** **0:cumSum(**
dayOfWk(*year,month,day***)**	Returns an integer from 1 to 7, with each integer representing a day of the week. Use **dayOfWk(** to determine on which day of the week a particular date would occur. The *year* must be 4 digits; *month* and *day* can be 1 or 2 digit.	[2nd] [CATALOG] **dayOfWk(** **1:Sunday** **2:Monday** **3:Tuesday...**
dbd(*date1,date2***)**	Calculates the number of days between *date1* and *date2* using the actual-day-count method.	[APPS] **1:Finance** **CALC** **D:dbd(**
value▸**Dec**	Displays a real or complex number, expression, list, or matrix in decimal format.	[MATH] **MATH** **2:▸Dec**
Degree	Sets degree angle mode.	† [MODE] **Degree**
DelVar *variable*	Deletes from memory the contents of *variable*.	† [PRGM] **CTL** **G:DelVar**
DependAsk	Sets table to ask for dependent-variable values.	† [2nd] [TBLSET] **Depend: Ask**
DependAuto	Sets table to generate dependent-variable values automatically.	† [2nd] [TBLSET] **Depend: Auto**

Function or Instruction/Arguments	Result	Key or Keys/Menu or Screen/Item
det(*matrix***)**	Returns determinant of *matrix*.	[2nd] [MATRIX] **MATH** **1:det(**
DiagnosticOff	Sets diagnostics-off mode; **r**, **r**^{2}, and **R**^{2} are not displayed as regression model results.	[2nd] [CATALOG] **DiagnosticOff**
DiagnosticOn	Sets diagnostics-on mode; **r**, **r**^{2}, and **R**^{2} are displayed as regression model results.	[2nd] [CATALOG] **DiagnosticOn**
dim(*listname***)**	Returns the dimension of *listname*.	[2nd] [LIST] **OPS** **3:dim(**
dim(*matrixname***)**	Returns the dimension of *matrixname* as a list.	[2nd] [MATRIX] **MATH** **3:dim(**
length→**dim(***listname***)**	Assigns a new dimension (*length*) to a new or existing *listname*.	[2nd] [LIST] **OPS** **3:dim(**
{*rows,columns*}→ **dim(***matrixname***)**	Assigns new dimensions to a new or existing *matrixname*.	[2nd] [MATRIX] **MATH** **3:dim(**
Disp	Displays the home screen.	† [PRGM] **I/O** **3:Disp**
Disp [*valueA,valueB, valueC,...,value n*]	Displays each value.	† [PRGM] **I/O** **3:Disp**
DispGraph	Displays the graph.	† [PRGM] **I/O** **4:DispGraph**
DispTable	Displays the table.	† [PRGM] **I/O** **5:DispTable**

Function or Instruction/Arguments	Result	Key or Keys/Menu or Screen/Item
value▶**DMS**	Displays *value* in DMS format.	[2nd] [ANGLE] **ANGLE** **4:▶DMS**
Dot	Sets dot plotting mode; resets all **Y=** editor graph-style settings to ∵.	† [MODE] **Dot**
DrawF *expression*	Draws *expression* (in terms of **X**) on the graph.	[2nd] [DRAW] **DRAW** **6:DrawF**
DrawInv *expression*	Draws the inverse of *expression* by plotting **X** values on the y-axis and **Y** values on the x-axis.	[2nd] [DRAW] **DRAW** **8:DrawInv**
:**DS<**(*variable,value*) :*commandA* :*commands*	Decrements *variable* by 1; skips *commandA* if *variable* < *value*.	† [PRGM] **CTL** **B:DS<(**
e^(*power***)**	Returns **e** raised to *power*.	[2nd] [eˣ]
e^(*list***)**	Returns a list of **e** raised to a *list* of powers.	[2nd] [eˣ]
Exponent: *value*ᴇ*exponent*	Returns *value* times 10 to the *exponent*.	[2nd] [EE]
Exponent: *list*ᴇ*exponent*	Returns *list* elements times 10 to the *exponent*.	[2nd] [EE]
Exponent: *matrix*ᴇ*exponent*	Returns *matrix* elements times 10 to the *exponent*.	[2nd] [EE]
▶**Eff(***nominal rate, compounding periods***)**	Computes the effective interest rate.	[APPS] **1:Finance** **CALC** **C:▶Eff(**
Else *See* **If:Then:Else**		
End	Identifies end of **For(,** **If-Then-Else, Repeat,** or **While** loop.	† [PRGM] **CTL** **7:End**
Eng	Sets engineering display mode.	† [MODE] **Eng**

Function or Instruction/Arguments	Result	Key or Keys/Menu or Screen/Item
Equ▸String(Y= *var,***Str***n***)**	Converts the contents of a **Y=** *var* to a string and stores it in **Str***n*.	[2nd] [CATALOG] **Equ▸String(**
expr(*string***)**	Converts *string* to an expression and executes it.	[2nd] [CATALOG] **expr(**
ExpReg [*Xlistname, Ylistname,freqlist,regequ*]	Fits an exponential regression model to *Xlistname* and *Ylistname* with frequency *freqlist,* and stores the regression equation to *regequ*.	[STAT] **CALC 0:ExpReg**
ExprOff	Turns off the expression display during **TRACE**.	† [2nd] [FORMAT] **ExprOff**
ExprOn	Turns on the expression display during **TRACE**.	† [2nd] [FORMAT] **ExprOn**
Fcdf(*lowerbound, upperbound, numerator df, denominator df***)**	Computes the F distribution probability between *lowerbound* and *upperbound* for the specified *numerator df* (degrees of freedom) and *denominator df*.	[2nd] [DISTR] **DISTR 0:Fcdf(**
Fill(*value,matrixname***)**	Stores *value* to each element in *matrixname*.	[2nd] [MATRIX] **MATH 4:Fill(**
Fill(*value,listname***)**	Stores *value* to each element in *listname*.	[2nd] [LIST] **OPS 4:Fill(**
Fix #	Sets fixed-decimal mode for # of decimal places.	† [MODE] **0123456789** (select one)
Float	Sets floating decimal mode.	† [MODE] **Float**

Function or Instruction/Arguments	Result	Key or Keys/Menu or Screen/Item
fMax(*expression,variable, lower,upper*[*,tolerance*]**)**	Returns the value of *variable* where the local maximum of *expression* occurs, between *lower* and *upper*, with specified *tolerance*.	MATH **MATH 7:fMax(**
fMin(*expression,variable, lower,upper*[*,tolerance*]**)**	Returns the value of *variable* where the local minimum of *expression* occurs, between *lower* and *upper*, with specified *tolerance*.	MATH **MATH 6:fMin(**
fnInt(*expression,variable, lower,upper*[*,tolerance*]**)**	Returns the function integral of *expression* with respect to *variable*, between *lower* and *upper*, with specified *tolerance*.	MATH **MATH 9:fnInt(**
FnOff [*function#, function#,...,function n*]	Deselects all **Y=** functions or specified **Y=** functions.	VARS **Y-VARS 4:On/Off 2:FnOff**
FnOn [*function#, function#,...,function n*]	Selects all **Y=** functions or specified **Y=** functions.	VARS **Y-VARS 4:On/Off 1:FnOn**
:For(*variable,begin,end* [*,increment*]**)** :*commands* **:End** :*commands*	Executes *commands* through **End**, incrementing *variable* from *begin* by *increment* until *variable*>*end*.	† PRGM **CTL 4:For(**
fPart(*value***)**	Returns the fractional part or parts of a real or complex number, expression, list, or matrix.	MATH **NUM 4:fPart(**

Function or Instruction/Arguments	Result	Key or Keys/Menu or Screen/Item
F pdf(x,*numerator df, denominator df*)	Computes the F distribution probability between *lowerbound* and *upperbound* for the specified *numerator df* (degrees of freedom) and *denominator df*.	[2nd] [DISTR] **DISTR** **9:Fpdf(**
value▶**Frac**	Displays a real or complex number, expression, list, or matrix as a fraction simplified to its simplest terms.	[MATH] **MATH** **1:▶Frac**
Full	Sets full screen mode.	† [MODE] **Full**
Func	Sets function graphing mode.	† [MODE] **Func**
GarbageCollect	Displays the garbage collection menu to allow cleanup of unused archive memory.	[2nd] [CATALOG] **GarbageCollect**
gcd(valueA,valueB**)**	Returns the greatest common divisor of *valueA* and *valueB*, which can be real numbers or lists.	[MATH] **NUM** **9:gcd(**
geometcdf(p,x**)**	Computes a cumulative probability at *x*, the number of the trial on which the first success occurs, for the discrete geometric distribution with the specified probability of success *p*.	[2nd] [DISTR] **DISTR** **F:geometcdf(**

Function or Instruction/Arguments	Result	Key or Keys/Menu or Screen/Item
geometpdf(p,x**)**	Computes a probability at x, the number of the trial on which the first success occurs, for the discrete geometric distribution with the specified probability of success p.	[2nd] [DISTR] **DISTR** **E:geometpdf(**
Get(variable**)**	Gets data from the CBL 2™ or CBR™ System and stores it in variable.	† [PRGM] **I/O** **A:Get(**
GetCalc(variable[,portflag]**)**	Gets contents of variable on another TI-84 Plus and stores it to variable on the receiving TI-84 Plus. By default, the TI-84 Plus uses the USB port if it is connected. If the USB cable is not connected, it uses the I/O port. portflag=0 use USB port if connected; portflag=1 use USB port; portflag=2 use I/O port.	† [PRGM] **I/O** **0:GetCalc(**
getDate	Returns a list giving the date according to the current value of the clock. The list is in {year,month,day} format.	[2nd] [CATALOG] **getDate**
getDtFmt	Returns an integer representing the date format that is currently set on the device. 1 = M/D/Y 2 = D/M/Y 3 = Y/M/D	[2nd] [CATALOG] **getDtFmt**

Function or Instruction/Arguments	Result	Key or Keys/Menu or Screen/Item
getDtStr(*integer*)	Returns a string of the current date in the format specified by *integer*, where: 1 = M/D/Y 2 = D/M/Y 3 = Y/M/D	[2nd] [CATALOG] **getDtStr(**
getKey	Returns the key code for the current keystroke, or **0**, if no key is pressed.	† [PRGM] **I/O** **7:getKey**
getTime	Returns a list giving the time according to the current value of the clock. The list is in *{hour,minute,second}* format. The time is returned in the 24 hour format.	[2nd] [CATALOG] **getTime**
getTmFmt	Returns an integer representing the clock time format that is currently set on the device. 12 = 12 hour format 24 = 24 hour format	[2nd] [CATALOG] **getTmFmt**
getTmStr(*integer*)	Returns a string of the current clock time in the format specified by *integer*, where: 12 = 12 hour format 24 = 24 hour format	[2nd] [CATALOG] **getTmStr(**
Goto *label*	Transfers control to *label*.	† [PRGM] **CTL** **0:Goto**
GraphStyle(*function#*, *graphstyle#*)	Sets a *graphstyle* for *function#*.	† [PRGM] **CTL** **H:GraphStyle(**

Function or Instruction/Arguments	Result	Key or Keys/Menu or Screen/Item
GridOff	Turns off grid format.	† [2nd] [FORMAT] **GridOff**
GridOn	Turns on grid format.	† [2nd] [FORMAT] **GridOn**
G-T	Sets graph-table vertical split-screen mode.	† [MODE] **G-T**
Horiz	Sets horizontal split-screen mode.	† [MODE] **Horiz**
Horizontal *y*	Draws a horizontal line at *y*.	[2nd] [DRAW] **DRAW** **3:Horizontal**
identity(*dimension***)**	Returns the identity matrix of *dimension* rows x *dimension* columns.	[2nd] [MATRIX] **MATH** **5:identity(**
:If *condition* **:***commandA* **:***commands*	If *condition* = 0 (false), skips *commandA*.	† [PRGM] **CTL** **1:If**
:If *condition* **:Then** **:***commands* **:End** **:***commands*	Executes *commands* from **Then** to **End** if *condition* = 1 (true).	† [PRGM] **CTL** **2:Then**
:If *condition* **:Then** **:***commands* **:Else** **:***commands* **:End** **:***commands*	Executes *commands* from **Then** to **Else** if *condition* = 1 (true); from **Else** to **End** if *condition* = 0 (false).	† [PRGM] **CTL** **3:Else**
imag(*value***)**	Returns the imaginary (nonreal) part of a complex number or list of complex numbers.	[MATH] **CPX** **3:imag(**
IndpntAsk	Sets table to ask for independent-variable values.	† [2nd] [TBLSET] **Indpnt: Ask**

Function or Instruction/Arguments	Result	Key or Keys/Menu or Screen/Item
IndpntAuto	Sets table to generate independent-variable values automatically.	† [2nd] [TBLSET] **Indpnt: Auto**
Input	Displays graph.	† [PRGM] **I/O** **1:Input**
Input [*variable*] **Input** [*"text",variable*]	Prompts for value to store to *variable*.	† [PRGM] **I/O** **1:Input**
Input [**Str***n,variable*]	Displays **Str***n* and stores entered value to *variable*.	† [PRGM] **I/O** **1:Input**
inString(*string,substring* [,*start*]**)**	Returns the character position in *string* of the first character of *substring* beginning at *start*.	[2nd] [CATALOG] **inString(**
int(*value***)**	Returns the largest integer ≤ a real or complex number, expression, list, or matrix.	[MATH] **NUM** **5:int(**
ΣInt(*pmt1,pmt2* [,*roundvalue*]**)**	Computes the sum, rounded to *roundvalue*, of the interest amount between *pmt1* and *pmt2* for an amortization schedule.	[APPS] **1:Finance** **CALC** **A:ΣInt(**
invNorm(*area*[,μ,σ]**)**	Computes the inverse cumulative normal distribution function for a given *area* under the normal distribution curve specified by μ and σ.	[2nd] [DISTR] **DISTR** **3:invNorm(**
invT(*area,df***)**	Computes the inverse cumulative student-t probability function specified by degree of freedom, df for a given area under the curve.	[2nd] [DISTR] **DISTR** **4:invT(**

Function or Instruction/Arguments	Result	Key or Keys/Menu or Screen/Item
iPart(_value_**)**	Returns the integer part of a real or complex number, expression, list, or matrix.	[MATH] **NUM** **3:iPart(**
irr(_CF0,CFList_[,_CFFreq_]**)**	Returns the interest rate at which the net present value of the cash flow is equal to zero.	[APPS] **1:Finance** **CALC** **8:irr(**
:IS>(_variable,value_**)** :_commandA_ :_commands_	Increments _variable_ by 1; skips _commandA_ if _variable_>_value_.	† [PRGM] **CTL** **A:IS>(**
isClockOn	Identifies if clock is ON or OFF. Returns 1 if the clock is ON. Returns 0 if the clock is OFF.	[2nd] [CATALOG] **isClockOn**
∟_listname_	Identifies the next one to five characters as a user-created list name.	[2nd] [LIST] **OPS** **B:∟**
LabelOff	Turns off axes labels.	† [2nd] [FORMAT] **LabelOff**
LabelOn	Turns on axes labels.	† [2nd] [FORMAT] **LabelOn**
Lbl _label_	Creates a _label_ of one or two characters.	† [PRGM] **CTL** **9:Lbl**
lcm(_valueA,valueB_**)**	Returns the least common multiple of _valueA_ and _valueB_, which can be real numbers or lists.	[MATH] **NUM** **8:lcm(**
length(_string_**)**	Returns the number of characters in _string_.	[2nd] [CATALOG] **length(**
Line(_X1,Y1,X2,Y2_**)**	Draws a line from (_X1,Y1_) to (_X2,Y2_).	[2nd] [DRAW] **DRAW** **2:Line(**

Function or Instruction/Arguments	Result	Key or Keys/Menu or Screen/Item
Line(*X1,Y1,X2,Y2,***0)**	Erases a line from (*X1,Y1*) to (*X2,Y2*).	[2nd] [DRAW] **DRAW** **2:Line(**
LinReg(a+bx) [*Xlistname, Ylistname,freqlist, regequ*]	Fits a linear regression model to *Xlistname* and *Ylistname* with frequency *freqlist*, and stores the regression equation to *regequ*.	[STAT] **CALC** **8:LinReg(a+bx)**
LinReg(ax+b) [*Xlistname, Ylistname,freqlist, regequ*]	Fits a linear regression model to *Xlistname* and *Ylistname* with frequency *freqlist*, and stores the regression equation to *regequ*.	[STAT] **CALC** **4:LinReg(ax+b)**
LinRegTTest [*Xlistname, Ylistname,freqlist, alternative,regequ*]	Performs a linear regression and a *t*-test. *alternative*=‑1 is <; *alternative*=0 is ≠; *alternative*=1 is >.	† [STAT] **TESTS** **F:LinRegTTest**
LinRegTInt [*Xlistname, Ylistname,freqlist, confidence level, regequ*]	Performs a linear regression and computes the t confidence interval for the slope coefficient b.	† [STAT] **TESTS** **G:LinRegTInt**
ΔList(*list*)	Returns a list containing the differences between consecutive elements in *list*.	[2nd] [LIST] **OPS** **7:ΔList(**
List ▸ matr(*listname1,..., listname n,matrixname*)	Fills *matrixname* column by column with the elements from each specified *listname*.	[2nd] [LIST] **OPS** **0:List ▸ matr(**
ln(*value*)	Returns the natural logarithm of a real or complex number, expression, or list.	[LN]

Function or Instruction/Arguments	Result	Key or Keys/Menu or Screen/Item
LnReg [*Xlistname, Ylistname, freqlist, regequ*]	Fits a logarithmic regression model to *Xlistname* and *Ylistname* with frequency *freqlist*, and stores the regression equation to *regequ*.	STAT **CALC** **9:LnReg**
log(*value***)**	Returns logarithm of a real or complex number, expression, or list.	LOG
Logistic [*Xlistname, Ylistname, freqlist, regequ*]	Fits a logistic regression model to *Xlistname* and *Ylistname* with frequency *freqlist*, and stores the regression equation to *regequ*.	STAT **CALC** **B:Logistic**
Manual-Fit *equname*	Fits a linear equation to a scatter plot.	STAT **CALC** **D:Manual-Fit**
Matr▶list(*matrix, listnameA,…,listname n***)**	Fills each *listname* with elements from each column in *matrix*.	2nd [LIST] **OPS** **A:Matr▶list(**
Matr▶list(*matrix, column#,listname***)**	Fills a *listname* with elements from a specified *column#* in *matrix*.	2nd [LIST] **OPS** **A:Matr▶list(**
max(*valueA, valueB***)**	Returns the larger of *valueA* and *valueB*.	MATH **NUM** **7:max(**
max(*list***)**	Returns largest real or complex element in *list*.	2nd [LIST] **MATH** **2:max(**
max(*listA, listB***)**	Returns a real or complex list of the larger of each pair of elements in *listA* and *listB*.	2nd [LIST] **MATH** **2:max(**

Function or Instruction/Arguments	Result	Key or Keys/Menu or Screen/Item
max(*value,list***)**	Returns a real or complex list of the larger of *value* or each *list* element.	[2nd] [LIST] **MATH** **2:max(**
mean(*list[,freqlist]***)**	Returns the mean of *list* with frequency *freqlist*.	[2nd] [LIST] **MATH** **3:mean(**
median(*list[,freqlist]***)**	Returns the median of *list* with frequency *freqlist*.	[2nd] [LIST] **MATH** **4:median(**
Med-Med [*Xlistname,* *Ylistname,freqlist,* *regequ*]	Fits a median-median model to *Xlistname* and *Ylistname* with frequency *freqlist*, and stores the regression equation to *regequ*.	[STAT] **CALC** **3:Med-Med**
Menu("*title***","***text1***",** *label1[,...,***"***text7***",***label7***])**	Generates a menu of up to seven items during program execution.	† [PRGM] **CTL** **C:Menu(**
min(*valueA,valueB***)**	Returns smaller of *valueA* and *valueB*.	[MATH] **NUM** **6:min(**
min(*list***)**	Returns smallest real or complex element in *list*.	[2nd] [LIST] **MATH** **1:min(**
min(*listA,listB***)**	Returns real or complex list of the smaller of each pair of elements in *listA* and *listB*.	[2nd] [LIST] **MATH** **1:min(**
min(*value,list***)**	Returns a real or complex list of the smaller of *value* or each *list* element.	[2nd] [LIST] **MATH** **1:min(**
valueA **nCr** *valueB*	Returns the number of combinations of *valueA* taken *valueB* at a time.	[MATH] **PRB** **3:nCr**

Function or Instruction/Arguments	Result	Key or Keys/Menu or Screen/Item
value **nCr** *list*	Returns a list of the combinations of *value* taken each element in *list* at a time.	MATH **PRB** **3:nCr**
list **nCr** *value*	Returns a list of the combinations of each element in *list* taken *value* at a time.	MATH **PRB** **3:nCr**
listA **nCr** *listB*	Returns a list of the combinations of each element in *listA* taken each element in *listB* at a time.	MATH **PRB** **3:nCr**
nDeriv(*expression, variable,value[,ε]***)**	Returns approximate numerical derivative of *expression* with respect to *variable* at *value*, with specified ε.	MATH **MATH** **8:nDeriv(**
▸Nom(*effective rate, compounding periods***)**	Computes the nominal interest rate.	APPS **1:Finance** **CALC** **B:▸Nom(**
Normal	Sets normal display mode.	† MODE **Normal**
normalcdf(*lowerbound, upperbound[,μ,σ]***)**	Computes the normal distribution probability between *lowerbound* and *upperbound* for the specified μ and σ.	2nd [DISTR] **DISTR** **2:normalcdf(**
normalpdf(*x[,μ,σ]***)**	Computes the probability density function for the normal distribution at a specified *x* value for the specified μ and σ.	2nd [DISTR] **DISTR** **1:normalpdf(**
not(*value***)**	Returns **0** if *value* is ≠ 0. *value* can be a real number, expression, or list.	2nd [TEST] **LOGIC** **4:not(**

Function or Instruction/Arguments	Result	Key or Keys/Menu or Screen/Item
valueA **nPr** *valueB*	Returns the number of permutations of *valueA* taken *valueB* at a time.	[MATH] **PRB** **2:nPr**
value **nPr** *list*	Returns a list of the permutations of *value* taken each element in *list* at a time	[MATH] **PRB** **2:nPr**
list **nPr** *value*	Returns a list of the permutations of each element in *list* taken *value* at a time.	[MATH] **PRB** **2:nPr**
listA **nPr** *listB*	Returns a list of the permutations of each element in *listA* taken each element in *listB* at a time.	[MATH] **PRB** **2:nPr**
npv(*interest rate,CF0,* *CFList[,CFFreq]***)**	Computes the sum of the present values for cash inflows and outflows.	[APPS] **1:Finance** **CALC** **7:npv(**
valueA **or** *valueB*	Returns 1 if *valueA* or *valueB* is ≠ 0. *valueA* and *valueB* can be real numbers, expressions, or lists.	[2nd] [TEST] **LOGIC** **2:or**
Output(*row,column,* **"***text***")**	Displays *text* beginning at specified *row* and *column*.	† [PRGM] **I/O** **6:Output(**
Output(*row,column,* *value***)**	Displays *value* beginning at specified *row* and *column*.	† [PRGM] **I/O** **6:Output(**
Param	Sets parametric graphing mode.	† [MODE] **Par**
Pause	Suspends program execution until you press [ENTER].	† [PRGM] **CTL** **8:Pause**

Function or Instruction/Arguments	Result	Key or Keys/Menu or Screen/Item
Pause [*value*]	Displays *value*; suspends program execution until you press [ENTER].	† [PRGM] **CTL** **8:Pause**
Plot#(*type,Xlistname, Ylistname,mark*)	Defines **Plot**# (**1, 2,** or **3**) of *type* **Scatter** or **xyLine** for *Xlistname* and *Ylistname* using *mark*.	† [2nd] [STAT PLOT] **STAT PLOTS** **1:Plot1-** **2:Plot2-** **3:Plot3-**
Plot#(*type,Xlistname, freqlist*)	Defines **Plot**# (**1, 2,** or **3**) of *type* **Histogram** or **Boxplot** for *Xlistname* with frequency *freqlist*.	† [2nd] [STAT PLOT] **STAT PLOTS** **1:Plot1-** **2:Plot2-** **3:Plot3-**
Plot#(*type,Xlistname, freqlist,mark*)	Defines **Plot**# (**1, 2,** or **3**) of *type* **ModBoxplot** for *Xlistname* with frequency *freqlist* using *mark*.	† [2nd] [STAT PLOT] **STAT PLOTS** **1:Plot1-** **2:Plot2-** **3:Plot3-**
Plot#(*type,datalistname, data axis,mark*)	Defines **Plot**# (**1, 2,** or **3**) of *type* **NormProbPlot** for *datalistname* on *data axis* using *mark*. *data axis* can be **X** or **Y**.	† [2nd] [STAT PLOT] **STAT PLOTS** **1:Plot1-** **2:Plot2-** **3:Plot3-**
PlotsOff [**1,2,3**]	Deselects all stat plots or one or more specified stat plots (**1, 2,** or **3**).	[2nd] [STAT PLOT] **STAT PLOTS** **4:PlotsOff**
PlotsOn [**1,2,3**]	Selects all stat plots or one or more specified stat plots (**1, 2,** or **3**).	[2nd] [STAT PLOT] **STAT PLOTS** **5:PlotsOn**
Pmt_Bgn	Specifies an annuity due, where payments occur at the beginning of each payment period.	[APPS] **1:Finance** **CALC** **F:Pmt_Bgn**
Pmt_End	Specifies an ordinary annuity, where payments occur at the end of each payment period.	[APPS] **1:Finance** **CALC** **E:Pmt_End**

Function or Instruction/Arguments	Result	Key or Keys/Menu or Screen/Item
poissoncdf(μ**,**x**)**	Computes a cumulative probability at x for the discrete Poisson distribution with specified mean μ.	[2nd] [DISTR] **DISTR** **D:poissoncdf(**
poissonpdf(μ**,**x**)**	Computes a probability at x for the discrete Poisson distribution with the specified mean μ.	[2nd] [DISTR] **DISTR** **C:poissonpdf(**
Polar	Sets polar graphing mode.	† [MODE] **Pol**
complex value **▶Polar**	Displays *complex value* in polar format.	[MATH] **CPX** **7▶Polar**
PolarGC	Sets polar graphing coordinates format.	† [2nd] [FORMAT] **PolarGC**
prgm*name*	Executes the program *name*.	† [PRGM] **CTRL** **D:prgm**
ΣPrn(*pmt1*,*pmt2* [,*roundvalue*]**)**	Computes the sum, rounded to *roundvalue*, of the principal amount between *pmt1* and *pmt2* for an amortization schedule.	[APPS] 1:Finance **CALC** **0:ΣPrn(**
prod(*list*[,*start*,*end*]**)**	Returns product of *list* elements between *start* and *end*.	[2nd] [LIST] **MATH** **6:prod(**
Prompt *variableA* [,*variableB*,...,*variable n*]	Prompts for value for *variableA*, then *variableB*, and so on.	† [PRGM] **I/O** **2:Prompt**
1-PropZInt(*x*,*n* [,*confidence level*]**)**	Computes a one-proportion z confidence interval.	† [STAT] **TESTS** **A:1-PropZInt(**
2-PropZInt(*x1*,*n1*,*x2*,*n2* [,*confidence level*]**)**	Computes a two-proportion z confidence interval.	† [STAT] **TESTS** **B:2-PropZInt(**

Function or Instruction/Arguments	Result	Key or Keys/Menu or Screen/Item
1-PropZTest(*p0,x,n*** [,***alternative,drawflag***])**	Computes a one-proportion z test. *alternative*=-**1** is <; *alternative*=**0** is ≠; *alternative*=**1** is >. *drawflag*=**1** draws results; *drawflag*=**0** calculates results.	† [STAT] **TESTS** **5:1-PropZTest(**
2-PropZTest(*x1,n1,x2,n2*** [,***alternative,drawflag***])**	Computes a two-proportion z test. *alternative*=-**1** is <; *alternative*=**0** is ≠; *alternative*=**1** is >. *drawflag*=**1** draws results; *drawflag*=**0** calculates results.	† [STAT] **TESTS** **6:2-PropZTest(**
Pt-Change(*x,y***)**	Reverses a point at (x,y).	[2nd] [DRAW] **POINTS** **3:Pt-Change(**
Pt-Off(*x,y*[,*mark*]**)**	Erases a point at (x,y) using *mark*.	[2nd] [DRAW] **POINTS** **2:Pt-Off(**
Pt-On(*x,y*[,*mark*]**)**	Draws a point at (x,y) using *mark*.	[2nd] [DRAW] **POINTS** **1:Pt-On(**
PwrReg [*Xlistname, Ylistname,freqlist, regequ*]	Fits a power regression model to *Xlistname* and *Ylistname* with frequency *freqlist*, and stores the regression equation to *regequ*.	[STAT] **CALC** **A:PwrReg**
Pxl-Change(*row,column***)**	Reverses pixel at $(row,column)$; $0 \le row \le 62$ and $0 \le column \le 94$.	[2nd] [DRAW] **POINTS** **6:Pxl-Change(**
Pxl-Off(*row,column***)**	Erases pixel at $(row,column)$; $0 \le row \le 62$ and $0 \le column \le 94$.	[2nd] [DRAW] **POINTS** **5:Pxl-Off(**

Function or Instruction/Arguments	Result	Key or Keys/Menu or Screen/Item
Pxl-On(row,column**)**	Draws pixel at (row,column); $0 \leq row \leq 62$ and $0 \leq column \leq 94$.	[2nd] [DRAW] **POINTS** **4:Pxl-On(**
pxl-Test(row,column**)**	Returns 1 if pixel (row, column) is on, 0 if it is off; $0 \leq row \leq 62$ and $0 \leq column \leq 94$.	[2nd] [DRAW] **POINTS** **7:pxl-Test(**
P▸Rx(r,θ**)**	Returns **X**, given polar coordinates r and θ or a list of polar coordinates.	[2nd] [ANGLE] **ANGLE** **7:P▸Rx(**
P▸Ry(r,θ**)**	Returns **Y**, given polar coordinates r and θ or a list of polar coordinates.	[2nd] [ANGLE] **ANGLE** **8:P▸Ry(**
QuadReg [Xlistname, Ylistname,freqlist, regequ]	Fits a quadratic regression model to Xlistname and Ylistname with frequency freqlist, and stores the regression equation to regequ.	[STAT] **CALC** **5:QuadReg**
QuartReg [Xlistname, Ylistname,freqlist, regequ]	Fits a quartic regression model to Xlistname and Ylistname with frequency freqlist, and stores the regression equation to regequ.	[STAT] **CALC** **7:QuartReg**
Radian	Sets radian angle mode.	† [MODE] **Radian**
rand[(numtrials)]	Returns a random number between 0 and 1 for a specified number of trials numtrials.	[MATH] **PRB** **1:rand**
randBin(numtrials,prob [,numsimulations]**)**	Generates and displays a random real number from a specified Binomial distribution.	[MATH] **PRB** **7:randBin(**

Function or Instruction/Arguments	Result	Key or Keys/Menu or Screen/Item
randInt(*lower,upper* [*,numtrials*]**)**	Generates and displays a random integer within a range specified by *lower* and *upper* integer bounds for a specified number of trials *numtrials*.	[MATH] **PRB** **5:randInt(**
randM(*rows,columns***)**	Returns a random matrix of *rows* (**1-99**) × *columns* (**1-99**).	[2nd] [MATRIX] **MATH** **6:randM(**
randNorm(μ,σ [*,numtrials*]**)**	Generates and displays a random real number from a specified Normal distribution specified by μ and σ for a specified number of trials *numtrials*.	[MATH] **PRB** **6:randNorm(**
r*e*^θ*i*	Sets the mode to polar complex number mode (**r***e*^θ*i*).	† [MODE] **r***e*^θ*i*
Real	Sets mode to display complex results only when you enter complex numbers.	† [MODE] **Real**
real(*value***)**	Returns the real part of a complex number or list of complex numbers.	[MATH] **CPX** **2:real(**
RecallGDB *n*	Restores all settings stored in the graph database variable **GDB***n*.	[2nd] [DRAW] **STO** **4:RecallGDB**
RecallPic *n*	Displays the graph and adds the picture stored in **Pic***n*.	[2nd] [DRAW] **STO** **2:RecallPic**
complex value ▶**Rect**	Displays *complex value* or list in rectangular format.	[MATH] **CPX** **6:▶Rect**
RectGC	Sets rectangular graphing coordinates format.	† [2nd] [FORMAT] **RectGC**

Function or Instruction/Arguments	Result	Key or Keys/Menu or Screen/Item
ref(_matrix_**)**	Returns the row-echelon form of a _matrix_.	[2nd] [MATRIX] **MATH** **A:ref(**
:Repeat _condition_ :_commands_ **:End** :_commands_	Executes _commands_ until _condition_ is true.	† [PRGM] **CTL** **6:Repeat**
Return	Returns to the calling program.	† [PRGM] **CTL** **E:Return**
round(_value_[,_#decimals_]**)**	Returns a number, expression, list, or matrix rounded to _#decimals_ (≤ 9).	[MATH] **NUM** **2:round(**
*row(_value,matrix,row_**)**	Returns a matrix with _row_ of _matrix_ multiplied by _value_ and stored in _row_.	[2nd] [MATRIX] **MATH** **E:*row(**
row+(_matrix,rowA,rowB_**)**	Returns a matrix with _rowA_ of _matrix_ added to _rowB_ and stored in _rowB_.	[2nd] [MATRIX] **MATH** **D:row+(**
*row+(_value,matrix, rowA,rowB_**)**	Returns a matrix with _rowA_ of _matrix_ multiplied by _value_, added to _rowB_, and stored in _rowB_.	[2nd] [MATRIX] **MATH** **F:*row+(**
rowSwap(_matrix,rowA, rowB_**)**	Returns a matrix with _rowA_ of _matrix_ swapped with _rowB_.	[2nd] [MATRIX] **MATH** **C:rowSwap(**
rref(_matrix_**)**	Returns the reduced row-echelon form of a _matrix_.	[2nd] [MATRIX] **MATH** **B:rref(**
R▶Pr(_x,y_**)**	Returns **R**, given rectangular coordinates x and y or a list of rectangular coordinates.	[2nd] [ANGLE] **ANGLE** **5:R▶Pr(**

Function or Instruction/Arguments	Result	Key or Keys/Menu or Screen/Item
R▶Pθ(x,y**)**	Returns θ, given rectangular coordinates x and y or a list of rectangular coordinates.	[2nd] [ANGLE] **ANGLE** **6:R▶Pθ(**
2-SampFTest [*listname1, listname2,freqlist1, freqlist2,alternative, drawflag*] (Data list input)	Performs a two-sample F test. *alternative*=‾1 is <; *alternative*=0 is ≠; *alternative*=1 is >. *drawflag*=1 draws results; *drawflag*=0 calculates results.	† [STAT] **TESTS** **E:2-SampFTest**
2-SampFTest $Sx1,n1,$ $Sx2,n2$[*,alternative, drawflag*] (Summary stats input)	Performs a two-sample F test. *alternative*=‾1 is <; *alternative*=0 is ≠; *alternative*=1 is >. *drawflag*=1 draws results; *drawflag*=0 calculates results.	† [STAT] **TESTS** **E:2-SampFTest**
2-SampTInt [*listname1, listname2, freqlist1,freqlist2, confidence level,pooled*] (Data list input)	Computes a two-sample t confidence interval. *pooled*=1 pools variances; *pooled*=0 does not pool variances.	† [STAT] **TESTS** **0:2-SampTInt**
2-SampTInt $\bar{x}1,Sx1,n1,$ $\bar{x}2,Sx2,n2$ [*,confidence level,pooled*] (Summary stats input)	Computes a two-sample t confidence interval. *pooled*=1 pools variances; *pooled*=0 does not pool variances.	† [STAT] **TESTS** **0:2-SampTInt**
2-SampTTest [*listname1, listname2,freqlist1, freqlist2,alternative, pooled,drawflag*] (Data list input)	Computes a two-sample t test. *alternative*=‾1 is <; *alternative*=0 is ≠; *alternative*=1 is >. *pooled*=1 pools variances; *pooled*=0 does not pool variances. *drawflag*=1 draws results; *drawflag*=0 calculates results.	† [STAT] **TESTS** **4:2-SampTTest**

Function or Instruction/Arguments	Result	Key or Keys/Menu or Screen/Item
2-SampTTest $\bar{x}1,Sx1,n1,$ $v2,Sx2,n2[,alternative,$ $pooled,drawflag]$ (Summary stats input)	Computes a two-sample t test. *alternative*=**-1** is **<**; *alternative*=**0** is **≠**; *alternative*=**1** is **>**. *pooled*=**1** pools variances; *pooled*=**0** does not pool variances. *drawflag*=**1** draws results; *drawflag*=**0** calculates results.	† [STAT] **TESTS** **4:2-SampTTest**
2-SampZInt(σ_1,σ_2 [,*listname1,listname2,* *freqlist1,freqlist2,* *confidence level*]**)** (Data list input)	Computes a two-sample z confidence interval.	† [STAT] **TESTS** **9:2-SampZInt(**
2-SampZInt($\sigma_1,\sigma_2,$ $\bar{x}1,n1,\bar{x}2,n2$ [,*confidence level*]**)** (Summary stats input)	Computes a two-sample z confidence interval.	† [STAT] **TESTS** **9:2-SampZInt(**
2-SampZTest(σ_1,σ_2 [,*listname1,listname2,* *freqlist1,freqlist2,* *alternative,drawflag*]**)** (Data list input)	Computes a two-sample z test. *alternative*=**-1** is **<**; *alternative*=**0** is **≠**; *alternative*=**1** is **>**. *drawflag*=**1** draws results; *drawflag*=**0** calculates results.	† [STAT] **TESTS** **3:2-SampZTest(**
2-SampZTest($\sigma_1,\sigma_2,$ $\bar{x}1,n1,\bar{x}2,n2$ [,*alternative,drawflag*]**)** (Summary stats input)	Computes a two-sample z test. *alternative*=**-1** is **<**; *alternative*=**0** is **≠**; *alternative*=**1** is **>**. *drawflag*=**1** draws results; *drawflag*=**0** calculates results.	† [STAT] **TESTS** **3:2-SampZTest(**
Sci	Sets scientific notation display mode.	† [MODE] **Sci**

Function or Instruction/Arguments	Result	Key or Keys/Menu or Screen/Item
Select(Xlistname, Ylistname**)**	Selects one or more specific data points from a scatter plot or xyLine plot (only), and then store•s the selected data points to two new lists, Xlistname and Ylistname.	[2nd] [LIST] **OPS** **8:Select(**
Send(variable**)**	Sends contents of variable to the CBL 2™ or CBR™ System.	† [PRGM] **I/O** **B:Send(**
seq(expression,variable, begin,end[,increment]**)**	Returns list created by evaluating expression with regard to variable, from begin to end by increment.	[2nd] [LIST] **OPS** **5:seq(**
Seq	Sets sequence graphing mode.	† [MODE] **Seq**
Sequential	Sets mode to graph functions sequentially.	† [MODE] **Sequential**
setDate(year,month,day**)**	Sets the date using a year, month, day format. The year must be 4 digits; month and day can be 1 or 2 digit.	[2nd] [CATALOG] **setDate(**
setDtFmt(integer**)**	Sets the date format. 1 = M/D/Y 2 = D/M/Y 3 = Y/M/D	[2nd] [CATALOG] **setDtFmt(**
setTime(hour,minute, second**)**	Sets the time using an hour, minute, second format. The hour must be in 24 hour format, in which 13 = 1 p.m.	[2nd] [CATALOG] **setTime(**
setTmFmt(integer**)**	Sets the time format. 12 = 12 hour format 24 = 24 hour format	[2nd] [CATALOG] **setTmFmt(**

Function or Instruction/Arguments	Result	Key or Keys/Menu or Screen/Item
SetUpEditor	Removes all list names from the stat list editor, and then restores list names **L1** through **L6** to columns **1** through **6**.	STAT **EDIT** **5:SetUpEditor**
SetUpEditor *listname1 [,listname2,..., listname20]*	Removes all list names from the stat list editor, then sets it up to display one or more *listnames* in the specified order, starting with column **1**.	STAT **EDIT** **5:SetUpEditor**
Shade(*lowerfunc, upperfunc[,Xleft,Xright, pattern,patres]***)**	Draws *lowerfunc* and *upperfunc* in terms of **X** on the current graph and uses *pattern* and *patres* to shade the area bounded by *lowerfunc, upperfunc, Xleft,* and *Xright.*	2nd [DRAW] **DRAW** **7:Shade(**
Shadeχ^2(*lowerbound, upperbound,df***)**	Draws the density function for the χ^2 distribution specified by degrees of freedom *df* and shades the area between *lowerbound* and *upperbound.*	2nd [DISTR] **DRAW** **3:Shadeχ^2(**
ShadeF(*lowerbound, upperbound, numerator df, denominator df***)**	Draws the density function for the F distribution specified by *numerator df* and *denominator df* and shades the area between *lowerbound* and *upperbound.*	2nd [DISTR] **DRAW** **4:ShadeF(**
ShadeNorm(*lowerbound, upperbound[,μ,σ]***)**	Draws the normal density function specified by μ and σ and shades the area between *lowerbound* and *upperbound.*	2nd [DISTR] **DRAW** **1:ShadeNorm(**

Function or Instruction/Arguments	Result	Key or Keys/Menu or Screen/Item
Shade_t(*lowerbound, upperbound,df***)**	Draws the density function for the Student-t distribution specified by degrees of freedom df, and shades the area between *lowerbound* and *upperbound*.	[2nd] [DISTR] **DRAW** **2:Shade_t(**
Simul	Sets mode to graph functions simultaneously.	† [MODE] **Simul**
sin(*value***)**	Returns the sine of a real number, expression, or list.	[SIN]
sin⁻¹(*value***)**	Returns the arcsine of a real number, expression, or list.	[2nd] [SIN⁻¹]
sinh(*value***)**	Returns the hyperbolic sine of a real number, expression, or list.	[2nd] [CATALOG] **sinh(**
sinh⁻¹ (*value***)**	Returns the hyperbolic arcsine of a real number, expression, or list.	[2nd] [CATALOG] **sinh⁻¹(**
SinReg [*iterations, Xlistname,Ylistname, period,regequ*]	Attempts *iterations* times to fit a sinusoidal regression model to *Xlistname* and *Ylistname* using a *period* guess, and stores the regression equation to *regequ*.	[STAT] **CALC** **C:SinReg**
solve(*expression,variable , guess,{lower,upper}***)**	Solves *expression* for *variable*, given an initial *guess* and *lower* and *upper* bounds within which the solution is sought.	† [MATH] **MATH** **0:solve(**
SortA(*listname***)**	Sorts elements of *listname* in ascending order.	[2nd] [LIST] **OPS** **1:SortA(**

Function or Instruction/Arguments	Result	Key or Keys/Menu or Screen/Item
SortA(_keylistname, dependlist1[,dependlist2, ...,dependlist n]_**)**	Sorts elements of _keylistname_ in ascending order, then sorts each _dependlist_ as a dependent list.	[2nd] [LIST] **OPS** **1:SortA(**
SortD(_listname_**)**	Sorts elements of _listname_ in descending order.	[2nd] [LIST] **OPS** **2:SortD(**
SortD(_keylistname,dependlist1[,dependlist2, ..., dependlist n]_**)**	Sorts elements of _keylistname_ in descending order, then sorts each _dependlist_ as a dependent list.	[2nd] [LIST] **OPS** **2:SortD(**
startTmr	Starts the clock timer. Store or note the displayed value, and use it as the argument for **checkTmr( )** to check the elapsed time.	[2nd] [CATALOG] **startTmr**
stdDev(_list[,freqlist]_**)**	Returns the standard deviation of the elements in _list_ with frequency _freqlist_.	[2nd] [LIST] **MATH** **7:stdDev(**
Stop	Ends program execution; returns to home screen.	† [PRGM] **CTL** **F:Stop**
Store: _value_→_variable_	Stores _value_ in _variable_.	[STO▸]
StoreGDB _n_	Stores current graph in database **GDB**_n_.	[2nd] [DRAW] **STO** **3:StoreGDB**
StorePic _n_	Stores current picture in picture **Pic**_n_.	[2nd] [DRAW] **STO** **1:StorePic**
String▸Equ(_string,_**Y=**_var_**)**	Converts _string_ into an equation and stores it in **Y=** _var_.	[2nd] [CATALOG] **String▸Equ(**

Function or Instruction/Arguments	Result	Key or Keys/Menu or Screen/Item
sub(*string,begin,length*)	Returns a string that is a subset of another *string*, from *begin* to *length*.	2nd [CATALOG] **sub(**
sum(*list[,start,end]*)	Returns the sum of elements of *list* from *start* to *end*.	2nd [LIST] **MATH** **5:sum(**
tan(*value*)	Returns the tangent of a real number, expression, or list.	[TAN]
tan^{-1}(*value*)	Returns the arctangent of a real number, expression, or list.	2nd [TAN⁻¹]
Tangent(*expression,value*)	Draws a line tangent to *expression* at **X**=*value*.	2nd [DRAW] **DRAW** **5:Tangent(**
tanh(*value*)	Returns hyperbolic tangent of a real number, expression, or list.	2nd [CATALOG] **tanh(**
tanh^{-1}(*value*)	Returns the hyperbolic arctangent of a real number, expression, or list.	2nd [CATALOG] **tanh**$^{-1}$**(**
tcdf(*lowerbound, upperbound,df*)	Computes the Student-*t* distribution probability between *lowerbound* and *upperbound* for the specified degrees of freedom *df*.	2nd [DISTR] **DISTR** **6:tcdf(**
Text(*row,column,text1, text2,...,text n*)	Writes *text* on graph beginning at pixel (*row,column*), where $0 \leq row \leq 57$ and $0 \leq column \leq 94$.	2nd [DRAW] **DRAW** **0:Text(**
Then *See* **If:Then**		

Appendix A: Functions and Instructions

Function or Instruction/Arguments	Result	Key or Keys/Menu or Screen/Item
Time	Sets sequence graphs to plot with respect to time.	† [2nd] [FORMAT] **Time**
timeCnv(seconds**)**	Converts seconds to units of time that can be more easily understood for evaluation. The list is in {days,hours,minutes,seconds} format.	[2nd] [CATALOG] **timeCnv**
TInterval [listname, freqlist,confidence level] (Data list input)	Computes a t confidence interval.	† [STAT] **TESTS** **8:TInterval**
TInterval $\bar{x}$,Sx,n [,confidence level] (Summary stats input)	Computes a t confidence interval.	† [STAT] **TESTS** **8:TInterval**
tpdf(x,df**)**	Computes the probability density function (pdf) for the Student-t distribution at a specified x value with specified degrees of freedom df.	[2nd] [DISTR] **DISTR** **5:tpdf(**
Trace	Displays the graph and enters **TRACE** mode.	[TRACE]
T-Test $\mu0$[,listname, freqlist,alternative, drawflag] (Data list input)	Performs a t test with frequency freqlist. alternative=-1 is <; alternative=0 is ≠; alternative=1 is >. drawflag=1 draws results; drawflag=0 calculates results.	† [STAT] **TESTS** **2:T-Test**
T-Test $\mu0$, $\bar{x}$,Sx,n [,alternative,drawflag] (Summary stats input)	Performs a t test with frequency freqlist. alternative=-1 is <; alternative=0 is ≠; alternative=1 is >. drawflag=1 draws results; drawflag=0 calculates results.	† [STAT] **TESTS** **2:T-Test**

Function or Instruction/Arguments	Result	Key or Keys/Menu or Screen/Item
tvm_FV[**(N,I%,**PV,PMT, P/Y,C/Y)]	Computes the future value.	APPS **1:Finance** **CALC** **6:tvm_FV**
tvm_I%[**(N,**PV,PMT,FV, P/Y,C/Y)]	Computes the annual interest rate.	APPS **1:Finance** **CALC** **3:tvm_I%**
tvm_N[(I%,PV,PMT,FV, P/Y,C/Y)]	Computes the number of payment periods.	APPS **1:Finance** **CALC** **5:tvm_N**
tvm_Pmt[**(N,I%,**PV,FV, P/Y,C/Y)]	Computes the amount of each payment.	APPS **1:Finance** **CALC** **2:tvm_Pmt**
tvm_PV[**(N,I%,**PMT,FV, P/Y,C/Y)]	Computes the present value.	APPS **1:Finance** **CALC** **4:tvm_PV**
UnArchive	Moves the specified variables from the user data archive memory to RAM. To archive variables, use **Archive**.	2nd [MEM] **6:UnArchive**
uvAxes	Sets sequence graphs to plot **u**(n) on the x-axis and **v**(n) on the y-axis.	† 2nd [FORMAT] **uv**
uwAxes	Sets sequence graphs to plot **u**(n) on the x-axis and **w**(n) on the y-axis.	† 2nd [FORMAT] **uw**
1-Var Stats [*Xlistname, freqlist*]	Performs one-variable analysis on the data in *Xlistname* with frequency *freqlist*.	STAT **CALC** **1:1-Var Stats**
2-Var Stats [*Xlistname, Ylistname,freqlist*]	Performs two-variable analysis on the data in *Xlistname* and *Ylistname* with frequency *freqlist*.	STAT **CALC** **2:2-Var Stats**

Function or Instruction/Arguments	Result	Key or Keys/Menu or Screen/Item
variance(_list_[,_freqlist_]**)**	Returns the variance of the elements in _list_ with frequency _freqlist_.	[2nd] [LIST] **MATH** **8:variance(**
Vertical _x_	Draws a vertical line at _x_.	[2nd] [DRAW] **DRAW** **4:Vertical**
vwAxes	Sets sequence graphs to plot **v**(_n_) on the x-axis and **w**(_n_) on the y-axis.	† [2nd] [FORMAT] **vw**
Web	Sets sequence graphs to trace as webs.	† [2nd] [FORMAT] **Web**
:While _condition_ **:**_commands_ **:End** **:**_command_	Executes _commands_ while _condition_ is true.	† [PRGM] **CTL** **5:While**
valueA **xor** _valueB_	Returns 1 if only _valueA_ or _valueB_ = 0. _valueA_ and _valueB_ can be real numbers, expressions, or lists.	[2nd] [TEST] **LOGIC** **3:xor**
ZBox	Displays a graph, lets you draw a box that defines a new viewing window, and updates the window.	† [ZOOM] **ZOOM** **1:ZBox**
ZDecimal	Adjusts the viewing window so that ∆**X=0.1** and ∆**Y=0.1**, and displays the graph screen with the origin centered on the screen.	† [ZOOM] **ZOOM** **4:ZDecimal**
ZInteger	Redefines the viewing window using these dimensions: ∆**X=1** **Xscl=10** ∆**Y=1** **Yscl=10**	† [ZOOM] **ZOOM** **8:ZInteger**

Function or Instruction/Arguments	Result	Key or Keys/Menu or Screen/Item
ZInterval σ[,*listname,* *freqlist,confidence level*] (Data list input)	Computes a z confidence interval.	† STAT **TESTS** **7:ZInterval**
ZInterval σ,x̄,*n* [,*confidence level*] (Summary stats input)	Computes a z confidence interval.	† STAT **TESTS** **7:ZInterval**
Zoom In	Magnifies the part of the graph that surrounds the cursor location.	† ZOOM **ZOOM** **2:Zoom In**
Zoom Out	Displays a greater portion of the graph, centered on the cursor location.	† ZOOM **ZOOM** **3:Zoom Out**
ZoomFit	Recalculates **Ymin** and **Ymax** to include the minimum and maximum **Y** values, between **Xmin** and **Xmax**, of the selected functions and replots the functions.	† ZOOM **ZOOM** **0:ZoomFit**
ZoomRcl	Graphs the selected functions in a user-defined viewing window.	† ZOOM **MEMORY** **3:ZoomRcl**
ZoomStat	Redefines the viewing window so that all statistical data points are displayed.	† ZOOM **ZOOM** **9:ZoomStat**
ZoomSto	Immediately stores the current viewing window.	† ZOOM **MEMORY** **2:ZoomSto**
ZPrevious	Replots the graph using the window variables of the graph that was displayed before you executed the last **ZOOM** instruction.	† ZOOM **MEMORY** **1:ZPrevious**

Function or Instruction/Arguments	Result	Key or Keys/Menu or Screen/Item
ZSquare	Adjusts the **X** or **Y** window settings so that each pixel represents an equal width and height in the coordinate system, and updates the viewing window.	† ZOOM **ZOOM** **5:ZSquare**
ZStandard	Replots the functions immediately, updating the window variables to the default values.	† ZOOM **ZOOM** **6:ZStandard**
Z-Test($\mu 0$,σ[,*listname,* *freqlist,alternative,* *drawflag*]**)** (Data list input)	Performs a z test with frequency *freqlist*. *alternative*=-**1** is **<**; *alternative*=**0** is **≠**; *alternative*=**1** is **>**. *drawflag*=**1** draws results; *drawflag*=**0** calculates results.	† STAT **TESTS** **1:Z-Test(**
Z-Test($\mu 0$,σ,$\bar{x}$,n [*,alternative,drawflag*]**)** (Summary stats input)	Performs a z test. *alternative*=-**1** is **<**; *alternative*=**0** is **≠**; *alternative*=**1** is **>**. *drawflag*=**1** draws results; *drawflag*=**0** calculates results.	† STAT **TESTS** **1:Z-Test(**
ZTrig	Replots the functions immediately, updating the window variables to preset values for plotting trig functions.	† ZOOM **ZOOM** **7:ZTrig**
Factorial: *value***!**	Returns factorial of *value*.	MATH **PRB** **4:!**
Factorial: *list***!**	Returns factorial of *list* elements.	MATH **PRB** **4:!**

Function or Instruction/Arguments	Result	Key or Keys/Menu or Screen/Item
Degrees notation: *value*°	Interprets *value* as degrees; designates degrees in DMS format.	[2nd] [ANGLE] **ANGLE** **1:**°
Radian: *angle*ʳ	Interprets *angle* as radians.	[2nd] [ANGLE] **ANGLE** **3:**ʳ
Transpose: *matrix*ᵀ	Returns a matrix in which each element (row, column) is swapped with the corresponding element (column, row) of *matrix*.	[2nd] [MATRIX] **MATH** **2:**ᵀ
xthroot$^x\sqrt{}$*value*	Returns *xthroot* of *value*.	[MATH] **MATH** **5:**$^x\sqrt{}$
$x^{th}root$$^x\sqrt{}$*list*	Returns *xthroot* of *list* elements.	[MATH] **MATH** **5:**$^x\sqrt{}$
list$^x\sqrt{}$*value*	Returns *list* roots of *value*.	[MATH] **MATH** **5:**$^x\sqrt{}$
listA$^x\sqrt{}$*listB*	Returns *listA* roots of *listB*.	[MATH] **MATH** **5:**$^x\sqrt{}$
Cube: *value*³	Returns the cube of a real or complex number, expression, list, or square matrix.	[MATH] **MATH** **3:**³
Cube root: $^3\sqrt{}$(*value*)	Returns the cube root of a real or complex number, expression, or list.	[MATH] **MATH** **4:**³$\sqrt{}$

Function or Instruction/Arguments	Result	Key or Keys/Menu or Screen/Item
Equal: *valueA=valueB*	Returns 1 if *valueA = valueB*. Returns 0 if *valueA ≠ valueB*. *valueA* and *valueB* can be real or complex numbers, expressions, lists, or matrices.	[2nd] [TEST] **TEST** **1:=**
Not equal: *valueA≠valueB*	Returns 1 if *valueA ≠ valueB*. Returns 0 if *valueA = valueB*. *valueA* and *valueB* can be real or complex numbers, expressions, lists, or matrices.	[2nd] [TEST] **TEST** **2:≠**
Less than: *valueA<valueB*	Returns 1 if *valueA < valueB*. Returns 0 if *valueA ≥ valueB*. *valueA* and *valueB* can be real or complex numbers, expressions, or lists.	[2nd] [TEST] **TEST** **5:<**
Greater than: *valueA>valueB*	Returns 1 if *valueA > valueB*. Returns 0 if *valueA ≤ valueB*. *valueA* and *valueB* can be real or complex numbers, expressions, or lists.	[2nd] [TEST] **TEST** **3:>**
Less than or equal: *valueA≤valueB*	Returns 1 if *valueA ≤ valueB*. Returns 0 if *valueA > valueB*. *valueA* and *valueB* can be real or complex numbers, expressions, or lists.	[2nd] [TEST] **TEST** **6:≤**
Greater than or equal: *valueA≥valueB*	Returns 1 if *valueA ≥ valueB*. Returns 0 if *valueA < valueB*. *valueA* and *valueB* can be real or complex numbers, expressions, or lists.	[2nd] [TEST] **TEST** **4:≥**

Function or Instruction/Arguments	Result	Key or Keys/Menu or Screen/Item
Inverse: $value^{-1}$	Returns 1 divided by a real or complex number or expression.	$[x^{-1}]$
Inverse: $list^{-1}$	Returns 1 divided by $list$ elements.	$[x^{-1}]$
Inverse: $matrix^{-1}$	Returns $matrix$ inverted.	$[x^{-1}]$
Square: $value^2$	Returns $value$ multiplied by itself. $value$ can be a real or complex number or expression.	$[x^2]$
Square: $list^2$	Returns $list$ elements squared.	$[x^2]$
Square: $matrix^2$	Returns $matrix$ multiplied by itself.	$[x^2]$
Powers: $value \char`^ power$	Returns $value$ raised to $power$. $value$ can be a real or complex number or expression.	$[\char`^]$
Powers: $list \char`^ power$	Returns $list$ elements raised to $power$.	$[\char`^]$
Powers: $value \char`^ list$	Returns $value$ raised to $list$ elements.	$[\char`^]$
Powers: $matrix \char`^ power$	Returns $matrix$ elements raised to $power$.	$[\char`^]$
Negation: $-value$	Returns the negative of a real or complex number, expression, list, or matrix.	$[(\text{-})]$
Power of ten: **10^(**$value$**)**	Returns 10 raised to the $value$ power. $value$ can be a real or complex number or expression.	$[2nd]\,[10^x]$
Power of ten: **10^(**$list$**)**	Returns a list of 10 raised to the $list$ power.	$[2nd]\,[10^x]$

Function or Instruction/Arguments	Result	Key or Keys/Menu or Screen/Item
Square root: √(*value*)	Returns square root of a real or complex number, expression, or list.	[2nd] [√]
Multiplication: *valueA*∗*valueB*	Returns *valueA* times *valueB*.	[×]
Multiplication: *value*∗*list*	Returns *value* times each *list* element.	[×]
Multiplication: *list*∗*value*	Returns each *list* element times *value*.	[×]
Multiplication: *listA*∗*listB*	Returns *listA* elements times *listB* elements.	[×]
Multiplication: *value*∗*matrix*	Returns value times *matrix* elements.	[×]
Multiplication: *matrixA*∗*matrixB*	Returns *matrixA* times *matrixB*.	[×]
Division: *valueA*/*valueB*	Returns *valueA* divided by *valueB*.	[÷]
Division: *list*/*value*	Returns *list* elements divided by value.	[÷]
Division: *value*/*list*	Returns value divided by *list* elements.	[÷]
Division: *listA*/*listB*	Returns *listA* elements divided by *listB* elements.	[÷]
Addition: *valueA*+*valueB*	Returns *valueA* plus *valueB*.	[+]
Addition: *list*+*value*	Returns list in which *value* is added to each *list* element.	[+]
Addition: *listA*+*listB*	Returns *listA* elements plus *listB* elements.	[+]
Addition: *matrixA*+*matrixB*	Returns *matrixA* elements plus *matrixB* elements.	[+]

Function or Instruction/Arguments	Result	Key or Keys/Menu or Screen/Item
Concatenation: *string1+string2*	Concatenates two or more strings.	⊞
Subtraction: *valueA−valueB*	Subtracts *valueB* from *valueA*.	⊟
Subtraction: *value−list*	Subtracts *list* elements from *value*.	⊟
Subtraction: *list−value*	Subtracts *value* from *list* elements.	⊟
Subtraction: *listA−listB*	Subtracts *listB* elements from *listA* elements.	⊟
Subtraction: *matrixA−matrixB*	Subtracts *matrixB* elements from *matrixA* elements.	⊟
Minutes notation:*degrees°minutes 'seconds"*	Interprets *minutes* angle measurement as minutes.	2nd [ANGLE] **ANGLE 2:'**
Seconds notation: *degrees°minutes'seconds"*	Interprets *seconds* angle measurement as seconds.	ALPHA ["]

B

Appendix B: Reference Information

Variables

User Variables

The TI-84 Plus uses the variables listed below in various ways. Some variables are restricted to specific data types.

The variables **A** through **Z** and θ are defined as real or complex numbers. You may store to them. The TI-84 Plus can update **X**, **Y**, **R**, θ, and **T** during graphing, so you may want to avoid using these variables to store nongraphing data.

The variables (list names) **L1** through **L6** are restricted to lists; you cannot store another type of data to them.

The variables (matrix names) **[A]** through **[J]** are restricted to matrices; you cannot store another type of data to them.

The variables **Pic1** through **Pic9** and **Pic0** are restricted to pictures; you cannot store another type of data to them.

The variables **GDB1** through **GDB9** and **GDB0** are restricted to graph databases; you cannot store another type of data to them.

The variables **Str1** through **Str9** and **Str0** are restricted to strings; you cannot store another type of data to them.

Except for system variables, you can store any string of characters, functions, instructions, or variables to the functions **Y**n, (**1** through **9**, and **0**), **X**n**T/Y**n**T** (**1** through **6**), **r**n (**1** through **6**), **u**(n), **v**(n), and **w**(n) directly or through the **Y=** editor. The validity of the string is determined when the function is evaluated.

Archive Variables

You can store data, programs or any variable from RAM to user data archive memory where they cannot be edited or deleted inadvertantly. Archiving also allows you to free up RAM for variables that may require additional memory. The names of archived variables are preceded by an asterisk *"* ∗ *"* indicating they are in user data archive.

System Variables

The variables below must be real numbers. You may store to them. Since the TI-84 Plus can update some of them, as the result of a **ZOOM**, for example, you may want to avoid using these variables to store nongraphing data.

- **Xmin**, **Xmax**, **Xscl**, Δ**X**, **XFact**, **Tstep**, **PlotStart**, n**Min**, and other window variables.

- **ZXmin**, **ZXmax**, **ZXscl**, **ZTstep**, **ZPlotStart**, **Zu(**n**Min)**, and other **ZOOM** variables.

The variables below are reserved for use by the TI-84 Plus. You cannot store to them.

n, $\bar{x}$, **Sx**, σ**x**, **minX**, **maxX**, **Gy**, Σy^2, Σxy, **a**, **b**, **c**, **RegEQ**, **x1**, **x2**, **y1**, **z**, **t**, **F**, χ^2, $\hat{p}$, $\bar{x}$**1**, **Sx1**, **n1**, **lower**, **upper**, r^2, R^2 and other statistical variables.

Statistics Formulas

This section contains statistics formulas for the **Logistic** and **SinReg** regressions, **ANOVA**, **2-SampFTest**, and **2-SampTTest**.

Logistic

The logistic regression algorithm applies nonlinear recursive least-squares techniques to optimize the following cost function:

$$J = \sum_{i=1}^{N} \left(\frac{c}{1 + ae^{-bx_i}} - y_i \right)^2$$

which is the sum of the squares of the residual errors,

where: x = the independent variable list
y = the dependent variable list
N = the dimension of the lists

This technique attempts to estimate the constants a, b, and c recursively to make J as small as possible.

SinReg

The sine regression algorithm applies nonlinear recursive least-squares techniques to optimize the following cost function:

$$J = \sum_{i=1}^{N} [a\sin(bx_i + c) + d - y_i]^2$$

which is the sum of the squares of the residual errors,

where: x = the independent variable list
y = the dependent variable list
N = the dimension of the lists

This technique attempts to recursively estimate the constants a, b, c, and d to make J as small as possible.

ANOVA(

The **ANOVA F** statistic is:

$$F = \frac{FactorMS}{ErrorMS}$$

The mean squares (*MS*) that make up **F** are:

$$FactorMS = \frac{FactorSS}{Factordf}$$

$$ErrorMS = \frac{ErrorSS}{Errordf}$$

The sum of squares (*SS*) that make up the mean squares are:

$$FactorSS = \sum_{i=1}^{I} n_i(\bar{x}_i - \bar{x})^2$$

$$ErrorSS = \sum_{i=1}^{I} (n_i - 1)Sx_i{}^2$$

The degrees of freedom *df* that make up the mean squares are:

$$Factordf = I - 1 = \text{numerator} df \text{ for } \mathbf{F}$$

$$Errordf = \sum_{i=1}^{I} (n_i - 1) = \text{denominator} df \text{ for } \mathbf{F}$$

where:

I	=	number of populations
$\bar{x}_i$	=	the mean of each list
	=	the standard deviation of each list
Sxi	=	the length of each list
ni	=	the mean of all lists
$\bar{x}$		

2-SampFTest

Below is the definition for the **2-SampFTest**.

*Sx*1, *Sx*2	=	Sample standard deviations having $n_1 - 1$ and $n_2 - 1$ degrees of freedom *df*, respectively.
F	=	F-statistic = $\left(\dfrac{Sx1}{Sx2}\right)^2$
$df(x, n_1-1, n_2-1)$	=	F*pdf*( ) with degrees of freedom *df*, n_1-1, and n_2-1

Appendix B: Reference Information

$$p \quad = \quad \text{reported } p \text{ value}$$

2-SampF Test for the alternative hypothesis $\sigma_1 > \sigma_2$.

$$p = \int_F^\alpha f(x, n_1 - 1, n_2 - 1)dx$$

2-SampF Test for the alternative hypothesis $\sigma_1 < \sigma_2$.

$$p = \int_0^F f(x, n_1 - 1, n_2 - 1)dx$$

2-SampF Test for the alternative hypothesis $\sigma_1 \neq \sigma_2$. Limits must satisfy the following:

$$\frac{p}{2} = \int_0^{Lbnd} f(x, n_1 - 1, n_2 - 1)dx = \int_{Ubnd}^\infty f(x, n_1 - 1, n_2 - 1)dx$$

where: $[Lbnd, Ubnd]$ = lower and upper limits

The **F**-statistic is used as the bound producing the smallest integral. The remaining bound is selected to achieve the preceding integral's equality relationship.

2-SampTTest

The following is the definition for the **2-SampTTest**. The two-sample t statistic with degrees of freedom df is:

$$t = \frac{\bar{x}_1 - \bar{x}_2}{S}$$

where the computation of S and df are dependent on whether the variances are pooled. If the variances are not pooled:

$$S = \sqrt{\frac{Sx_1^2}{n_1} + \frac{Sx_2^2}{n_2}}$$

$$df = \frac{\left(\dfrac{Sx_1^2}{n_1} + \dfrac{Sx_2^2}{n_2}\right)^2}{\dfrac{1}{n_1 - 1}\left(\dfrac{Sx_1^2}{n_1}\right)^2 + \dfrac{1}{n_2 - 1}\left(\dfrac{Sx_2^2}{n_2}\right)^2}$$

otherwise:

$$Sx_p = \frac{(n_1 - 1)Sx_1^2 + (n_2 - 1)Sx_2^2}{df}$$

$$S = \sqrt{\frac{1}{n_1} + \frac{1}{n_2}Sx_p}$$

$$df = n_1 + n_2 - 2$$

and Sxp is the pooled variance.

Financial Formulas

This section contains financial formulas for computing time value of money, amortization, cash flow, interest-rate conversions, and days between dates.

Time Value of Money

$$i = [e^{(y \times \ln(x+1))}] - 1$$

where: $PMT \neq 0$

$y = C/Y \div P/Y$

$x = (.01 \times I\%) \div C/Y$

C/Y = compounding periods per year

P/Y = payment periods per year

$I\%$ = interest rate per year

$$i = (-FV \div PV)^{(1 \div N)} - 1$$

where: $PMT = 0$

The iteration used to compute i:

$$0 = PV + PMT \times G_i\left[\frac{1-(1+i)^{-N}}{i}\right] + FV \times (1+i)^{-N}$$

$$I\% = 100 \times C/Y \times [e^{(y \times \ln(x+1))} - 1]$$

where: $x = i$

$y = P/Y \div C/Y$

$$G_i = 1 + i \times k$$

where: $k = 0$ for end-of-period payments

$k = 1$ for beginning-of-period payments

$$N = \frac{\ln\left(\dfrac{PMT \times G_i - FV \times i}{PMT \times G_i + PV \times i}\right)}{\ln(1+i)}$$

where: $i \neq 0$

$$N = -(PV + FV) \div PMT$$

where: $i = 0$

$$PMT = \frac{-i}{G_i} \times \left[PV + \frac{PV + FV}{(1+i)^N - 1} \right]$$

where: $i \neq 0$

$$PMT = {}^-(PV + FV) \div N$$

where: $i = 0$

$$PV = \left[\frac{PMT \times G_i}{i} - FV \right] \times \frac{1}{(1+i)^N} - \frac{PMT \times G_i}{i}$$

where: $i \neq 0$

$$PV = {}^-(FV + PMT \times N)$$

where: $i = 0$

$$FV = \frac{PMT \times G_i}{i} - (1+i)^N \times \left(PV + \frac{PMT \times G_i}{i} \right)$$

where: $i \neq 0$

$$FV = {}^-(PV + PMT \times N)$$

where: $i = 0$

Amortization

If computing bal(), $pmt2 = npmt$

Let $bal(0) = RND(PV)$

Iterate from $m = 1$ to $pmt2$

$$\begin{cases} I_m = RND[RND12(-i \times bal(m-1))] \\ bal(m) = bal(m-1) - I_m + RND(PMT) \end{cases}$$

then:

$$bal(\ ) = bal(pmt2)$$

$$\Sigma Prn(\ ) = bal(pmt2) - bal(pmt1)$$

$$\Sigma Int(\ ) = (pmt2 - pmt1 + 1) \times RND(PMT) - \Sigma Prn(\ )$$

where: RND =   round the display to the number of decimal places selected

$RND12$ = round to 12 decimal places

Balance, principal, and interest are dependent on the values of **PMT, PV,** I%, and $pmt1$ and $pmt2$.

Cash Flow

$$npv(\ ) = CF_0 + \sum_{j=1}^{N} CF_j(1+i)^{-S_j-1}\frac{(1-(1+i)^{-n_j})}{i}$$

where: $S_j = \begin{cases} \displaystyle\sum_{i=1}^{j} n_i & j \geq 1 \\ 0 & j = 0 \end{cases}$

Net present value is dependent on the values of the initial cash flow (CF_0), subsequent cash flows (CF_j), frequency of each cash flow (n_j), and the specified interest rate (i).

$irr(\ ) = 100 \times i$, where i satisfies $npv(\ ) = 0$

Internal rate of return is dependent on the values of the initial cash flow (CF_0) and subsequent cash flows (CF_j).

$i = I\% + 100$

Interest Rate Conversions

$$\blacktriangleright Eff = 100 \times (e^{CP \times \ln(x+1)} - 1)$$

where: $x = .01 \times Nom + CP$

$$\blacktriangleright Nom = 100 \times CP \times [e^{1 + CP \times \ln(x+1)} - 1]$$

where: x = $.01 \times Eff$

         Eff =   *effective rate*

         CP =   *compounding periods*

         Nom =   *nominal rate*

Days between Dates

With the **dbd(** function, you can enter or compute a date within the range Jan. 1, 1950, through Dec. 31, 2049.

Actual/actual day-count method (assumes actual number of days per month and actual number of days per year):

dbd((days between dates) = Number of Days II - Number of Days I

Number of Days I   = $(Y1\text{-}YB) \times 365$

                    +   (number of days MB to $M1$)

                    + $DT1$

                    + $\dfrac{(Y1 - YB)}{4}$

Number of Days II   = $(Y2\text{-}YB) \times 365$

                    +   (number of days MB to $M2$)

                    + $DT2$

                    + $\dfrac{(Y2 - YB)}{4}$

where: $M1$ =   month of first date
        $DT1$ =   day of first date
        $Y1$ =   year of first date
        $M2$ =   month of second date
        $DT2$ =   day of second date
        $Y2$ =   year of second date
        MB =   base month (January)
        DB =   base day (1)
        YB =   base year (first year after leap year)

Important Things You Need to Know About Your TI-84 Plus

TI-84 Plus Results

There may be a number of reasons that your TI-84 Plus is not displaying the expected results; however, the most common solutions involve order of operations or mode settings. Your calculator uses an Equation Operating System (EOS) which evaluates the functions in an expression in the following order:

1. Functions that precede the argument, such as square root, sin(, or log(

2. Functions that are entered after the argument, such as exponents, factorial, r, °, and conversions

3. Powers and roots, such as 2^5, or 5*square root(32)

4. Permutations (nPr) and combinations (nCr)

5. Multiplication, implied multiplication, and division

6. Addition and subtraction

7. Relational functions, such as > or <

8. Logic operator and

9. Logic operators or and xor

Remember that EOS evaluates from left to right and calculations within parentheses are evaluated first. You should use parentheses where the rules of algebra may not be clear.

If you are using trigonometric functions or performing polar and rectangular conversions, the unexpected results may be caused by an angle mode setting. The Radian and Degree angle mode settings control how the TI-84 Plus interprets angle values.

To change the angle mode settings, follow these steps:

1. Press [MODE] to display the Mode settings.

2. Select **Degree** or **Radian**.

3. Press [ENTER] to save the angle mode setting.

ERR:DIM MISMATCH Error

Your TI-84 Plus displays the **ERR:DIM MISMATCH** error if you are trying to perform an operation that references one or more lists or matrices whose dimensions do not match. For example, multiplying L1*L2, where L1={1,2,3,4,5} and L2={1,2} produces an **ERR:DIM MISMATCH** error because the number of elements in L1 and L2 do not match.

ERR:INVALID DIM Error

The **ERR:INVALID DIM** error message may occur if you are trying to graph a function that does not involve the stat plot features. The error can be corrected by turning off the stat plots. To turn the stat plots off, press [2nd] [STAT PLOT] and then select **4:PlotsOff**.

Link-Receive L1 (or any file) to Restore Message

Your TI-84 Plus displays the **Link-Receive L1 (or any file) to Restore message** if it has been disabled for testing, and not re-enabled. To restore your calculator to full functionality after testing, link to another TI-84 Plus and transfer any file to the disabled calculator, or use TI Connect™ to download a file from your computer to your TI-84 Plus.

To transfer a file from another TI-84 Plus:

1. On the receiving unit, press [2nd] [LINK] and then select **RECEIVE**.

2. On the sending calculator, Press [2nd] [LINK].

3. Select a file to send by selecting a category, and then selecting a file to send.

4. Select **TRANSMIT** to send the file.

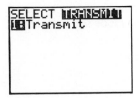

Contrast Feature

If the contrast setting is too dark (set to 9) or too dim (set to 0) the unit may appear as if it is malfunctioning or turned off. To adjust the contrast, press *and* release [2nd], and then press and hold △ or ▽.

TI-84 Plus Identification Code

Your graphing calculator has a unique identification (ID) code that you should record and keep. You can use this 14 digit ID to register your calculator at education.ti.com or identify your calculator in the event that it is lost or stolen. A valid ID includes numbers 0 through 9 and the letters A through F.

You can view the calculator's Operating System, Product Number, ID, and Certificate Revision Number from the **About** screen. To display the **About** screen, press [2nd] [MEM] and then select **1:About**.

```
TI-84 Plus Silver Edition
           2.30
PROD #: 0A-2-02-14
ID: 0A3C3-79DF1-E362


Help: education.ti.com
```

Your unique product ID code: _____

Backups

Your TI-84 Plus is similar to a computer, in that it stores files and Apps that are important to you. It is always a good idea to back up your graphing calculator device files and Apps using the TI Connect™ software and a USB computer cable. You can find the specific procedures for backing up your calculator's device files and Apps in the TI Connect™ Help file.

Apps

TI-84 Plus Software Applications (Apps) is software that you can add to your calculator in the same way you would add software to your computer. Apps let you customize your calculator for peak performance in specific areas of study. You can find apps for the TI-84 Plus at the TI Online Store at education.ti.com.

TI-Cares KnowledgeBase

The TI-Cares KnowledgeBase provides 24-hour access through the Web to find answers to frequently asked questions. The TI-Cares KnowledgeBase searches its repository of known solutions and presents you with the solutions that are most likely to solve your problem. You can search the TI-Cares KnowledgeBase at education.ti.com/support.

Error Conditions

When the TI-84 Plus detects an error, it returns an error message as a menu title, such as **ERR:SYNTAX** or **ERR:DOMAIN**. This table contains each error type, possible causes, and suggestions for correction. The error types listed in this table are each preceded by **ERR:** on your graphing calculator display. For example, you will see **ERR:ARCHIVED** as a menu title when your graphing calculator detects an **ARCHIVED** error type.

Error Type	Possible Causes and Suggested Remedies
ARCHIVED	You have attempted to use, edit, or delete an archived variable. For example, the expression dim(L1) produces an error if L1 is archived.
ARCHIVE FULL	You have attempted to archive a variable and there is not enough space in archive to receive it.
ARGUMENT	A function or instruction does not have the correct number of arguments. See Appendix A for function and instruction syntax.
	Appendix A displays the arguments and punctuation needed to execute the function or instruction. For example, **stdDev(**$list[,freqlist]$**)** is a function of the TI-84 Plus. The arguments are shown in italics. The arguments in brackets are optional and you need not type them. You must also be sure to separate multiple arguments with a comma (,). For example, **stdDev(**$list[,freqlist]$**)** might be entered as stdDev(L1) or stdDev(L1,L2) since the frequency list or $freqlist$ is optional.
BAD ADDRESS	You have attempted to send or receive an application and an error (e.g. electrical interference) has occurred in the transmission.
BAD GUESS	• In a **CALC** operation, you specified a **Guess** that is not between **Left Bound** and **Right Bound**.
	• For the **solve(** function or the equation solver, you specified a $guess$ that is not between $lower$ and $upper$.
	• Your guess and several points around it are undefined.
	Examine a graph of the function. If the equation has a solution, change the bounds and/or the initial guess.

Error Type	Possible Causes and Suggested Remedies
BOUND	• In a **CALC** operation or with **Select(**, you defined **Left Bound > Right Bound**. • In **fMin(, fMax(, solve(**, or the equation solver, you entered *lower ≥ upper*.
BREAK	You pressed the ON key to break execution of a program, to halt a **DRAW** instruction, or to stop evaluation of an expression.
DATA TYPE	You entered a value or variable that is the wrong data type. • For a function (including implied multiplication) or an instruction, you entered an argument that is an invalid data type, such as a complex number where a real number is required. See Appendix A and the appropriate chapter. • In an editor, you entered a type that is not allowed, such as a matrix entered as an element in the stat list editor. See the appropriate chapter. • You attempted to store an incorrect data type, such as a matrix, to a list.
DIM MISMATCH	Your calculator displays the **ERR:DIM MISMATCH** error if you are trying to perform an operation that references one or more lists or matrices whose dimensions do not match. For example, multiplying L1*L2, where L1={1,2,3,4,5} and L2={1,2} produces an **ERR:DIM MISMATCH** error because the number of elements in L1 and L2 do not match.
DIVIDE BY 0	• You attempted to divide by zero. This error is not returned during graphing. The TI-84 Plus allows for undefined values on a graph. • You attempted a linear regression with a vertical line.

Error Type	Possible Causes and Suggested Remedies
DOMAIN	• You specified an argument to a function or instruction outside the valid range. This error is not returned during graphing. The TI-84 Plus allows for undefined values on a graph. See Appendix A.
	• You attempted a logarithmic or power regression with a ⁻X or an exponential or power regression with a ⁻Y.
	• You attempted to compute **ΣPrn(** or **ΣInt(** with $pmt2 < pmt1$.
DUPLICATE	You attempted to create a duplicate group name.
Duplicate Name	A variable you attempted to transmit cannot be transmitted because a variable with that name already exists in the receiving unit.
EXPIRED	You have attempted to run an application with a limited trial period which has expired.
Error in Xmit	• The TI-84 Plus was unable to transmit an item. Check to see that the cable is firmly connected to both units and that the receiving unit is in receive mode.
	• You pressed ON to break during transmission.
	• You attempted to perform a backup from a TI-82 to a TI-84 Plus.
	• You attempted to transfer data (other than **L1** through **L6**) from a TI-84 Plus to a TI-82.
	• You attempted to transfer **L1** through **L6** from a TI-84 Plus to a TI-82 without using **5:Lists to TI82** on the **LINK SEND** menu.
ID NOT FOUND	This error occurs when the SendID command is executed but the proper graphing calculator ID cannot be found.
ILLEGAL NEST	• You attempted to use an invalid function in an argument to a function, such as **seq(** within *expression* for **seq(**.

Error Type	Possible Causes and Suggested Remedies
INCREMENT	• The increment in **seq(** is 0 or has the wrong sign. This error is not returned during graphing. The TI-84 Plus allows for undefined values on a graph. • The increment in a **For(** loop is 0.
INVALID	• You attempted to reference a variable or use a function where it is not valid. For example, **Y**n cannot reference **Y**, **Xmin**, **ΔX**, or **TblStart**. • You attempted to reference a variable or function that was transferred from the TI-82 and is not valid for the TI-84 Plus For example, you may have transferred **U**$n-$**1** to the TI-84 Plus from the TI-82 and then tried to reference it. • In **Seq** mode, you attempted to graph a phase plot without defining both equations of the phase plot. • In **Seq** mode, you attempted to graph a recursive sequence without having input the correct number of initial conditions. • In **Seq** mode, you attempted to reference terms other than $(n-$**1**) or $(n-$**2**). • You attempted to designate a graph style that is invalid within the current graph mode. • You attempted to use **Select(** without having selected (turned on) at least one xyLine or scatter plot.
INVALID DIM	• The **ERR:INVALID DIM** error message may occur if you are trying to graph a function that does not involve the stat plot features. The error can be corrected by turning off the stat plots. To turn the stat plots off, press [2nd] [STAT PLOT] and then select **4:PlotsOff**. • You specified a list dimension as something other than an integer between 1 and 999. • You specified a matrix dimension as something other than an integer between 1 and 99. • You attempted to invert a matrix that is not square.

Error Type	Possible Causes and Suggested Remedies
ITERATIONS	• The **solve(** function or the equation solver has exceeded the maximum number of permitted iterations. Examine a graph of the function. If the equation has a solution, change the bounds, or the initial guess, or both.
	• **irr(** has exceeded the maximum number of permitted iterations.
	• When computing I%, the maximum number of iterations was exceeded.
LABEL	The label in the **Goto** instruction is not defined with a **Lbl** instruction in the program.
LINK L1 (or any other file) to Restore	The calculator has been disabled for testing. To restore full functionality, use TI Connect™ to download a file to your calculator from your computer, or transfer any file to your calculator from another TI-84 Plus. (See the instructions under *Important Things to Know about your TI-84 Plus*, earlier in this chapter.)
MEMORY	Memory is insufficient to perform the instruction or function. You must delete items from memory before executing the instruction or function.
	Recursive problems return this error; for example, graphing the equation **Y1=Y1**.
	Branching out of an **If/Then**, **For(**, **While**, or **Repeat** loop with a **Goto** also can return this error because the **End** statement that terminates the loop is never reached.
MemoryFull	• You are unable to transmit an item because the receiving unit's available memory is insufficient. You may skip the item or exit receive mode.
	• During a memory backup, the receiving unit's available memory is insufficient to receive all items in the sending unit's memory. A message indicates the number of bytes the sending unit must delete to do the memory backup. Delete items and try again.

Error Type	Possible Causes and Suggested Remedies
MODE	You attempted to store to a window variable in another graphing mode or to perform an instruction while in the wrong mode; for example, **DrawInv** in a graphing mode other than **Func**.
NO SIGN CHNG	• The **solve(** function or the equation solver did not detect a sign change. • You attempted to compute I% when **FV**, (**N∗PMT**), and **PV** are all ≥ 0, or when **FV**, (**N∗PMT**), and **PV** are all ≤ 0. • You attempted to compute **irr(** when neither *CFList* nor *CFO* is > 0, or when neither *CFList* nor *CFO* is < 0.
NONREAL ANS	In **Real** mode, the result of a calculation yielded a complex result. This error is not returned during graphing. The TI-84 Plus allows for undefined values on a graph.
OVERFLOW	You attempted to enter, or you have calculated, a number that is beyond the range of the graphing calculator. This error is not returned during graphing. The TI-84 Plus allows for undefined values on a graph.
RESERVED	You attempted to use a system variable inappropriately. See Appendix A.
SINGULAR MAT	• A singular matrix (determinant = 0) is not valid as the argument for ⁻**1**. • The **SinReg** instruction or a polynomial regression generated a singular matrix (determinant = 0) because it could not find a solution, or a solution does not exist. This error is not returned during graphing. The TI-84 Plus allows for undefined values on a graph.
SINGULARITY	*expression* in the **solve(** function or the equation solver contains a singularity (a point at which the function is not defined). Examine a graph of the function. If the equation has a solution, change the bounds or the initial guess or both.

Error Type	Possible Causes and Suggested Remedies
STAT	You attempted a stat calculation with lists that are not appropriate. • Statistical analyses must have at least two data points. • **Med-Med** must have at least three points in each partition. • When you use a frequency list, its elements must be ≥ 0. • **(Xmax − Xmin) / Xscl** must be ≤ 47 for a histogram.
STAT PLOT	You attempted to display a graph when a stat plot that uses an undefined list is turned on.
SYNTAX	The command contains a syntax error. Look for misplaced functions, arguments, parentheses, or commas. Appendix A displays the arguments and punctuation needed to execute the function or instruction. For example, **stdDev(**_list_[,_freqlist_]**)** is a function of the TI-84 Plus. The arguments are shown in italics. The arguments in brackets are optional and you need not type them. You must also be sure to separate multiple arguments with a comma (,). For example **stdDev(**_list_[,_freqlist_]**)** might be entered as stdDev(L1) or stdDev(L1,L2) since the frequency list or _freqlist_ is optional.
TOL NOT MET	You requested a tolerance to which the algorithm cannot return an accurate result.
UNDEFINED	You referenced a variable that is not currently defined. For example, you referenced a stat variable when there is no current calculation because a list has been edited, or you referenced a variable when the variable is not valid for the current calculation, such as **a** after **Med-Med**.
VALIDATION	Electrical interference caused a link to fail or this graphing calculator is not authorized to run the application.

Appendix B: Reference Information

Error Type	Possible Causes and Suggested Remedies
VARIABLE	You have tried to archive a variable that cannot be archived or you have tried to unarchive an application or group.
	Examples of variables that cannot be archived include:
	• Real numbers **LRESID, R, T, X, Y, Theta**, Statistic variables under **Vars, STATISTICS** menu, **Yvars**, and the **AppIdList**.
VERSION	You have attempted to receive an incompatible variable version from another graphing calculator.
WINDOW RANGE	A problem exists with the window variables.
	• You defined **Xmax** ≤ **Xmin** or **Ymax** ≤ **Ymin**.
	• You defined θ**max** ≤ θ**min** and θ**step** > **0** (or vice versa).
	• You attempted to define **Tstep=0**.
	• You defined **Tmax** ≤ **Tmin** and **Tstep** > **0** (or vice versa).
	• Window variables are too small or too large to graph correctly. You may have attempted to zoom in or zoom out to a point that exceeds the TI-84 Plus's numerical range.
ZOOM	• A point or a line, instead of a box, is defined in **ZBox**.
	• A **ZOOM** operation returned a math error.

Accuracy Information

Computational Accuracy

To maximize accuracy, the TI-84 Plus carries more digits internally than it displays. Values are stored in memory using up to 14 digits with a two-digit exponent.

- You can store a value in the window variables using up to 10 digits (12 for **Xscl**, **Yscl**, **Tstep**, and θ**step**).

- Displayed values are rounded as specified by the mode setting with a maximum of 10 digits and a two-digit exponent.

- **RegEQ** displays up to 14 digits in **Float** mode. Using a fixed-decimal setting other than **Float** causes **RegEQ** results to be rounded and stored with the specified number of decimal places.

Xmin is the center of the leftmost pixel, **Xmax** is the center of the next-to-the-rightmost pixel. (The rightmost pixel is reserved for the busy indicator.) Δ**X** is the distance between the centers of two adjacent pixels.

- In **Full** screen mode, Δ**X** is calculated as (**Xmax** − **Xmin**) / 94. In **G-T** split-screen mode, Δ**X** is calculated as (**Xmax** − **Xmin**) / 46.

- If you enter a value for Δ**X** from the home screen or a program in **Full** screen mode, **Xmax** is calculated as **Xmin** + Δ**X** * 94. In **G-T** split-screen mode, **Xmax** is calculated as **Xmin** + Δ**X** * 46.

Ymin is the center of the next-to-the-bottom pixel; **Ymax** is the center of the top pixel. Δ**Y** is the distance between the centers of two adjacent pixels.

- In **Full** screen mode, Δ**Y** is calculated as (**Ymax** − **Ymin**) / 62. In **Horiz** split-screen mode, Δ**Y** is calculated as (**Ymax** − **Ymin**) / 30. In **G-T** split-screen mode, Δ**Y** is calculated as (**Ymax** − **Ymin**) / 50.

- If you enter a value for Δ**Y** from the home screen or a program in **Full** screen mode, **Ymax** is calculated as **Ymin** + Δ**Y** * 62. In **Horiz** split-screen mode, **Ymax** is calculated as **Ymin** + Δ**Y** * 30. In **G-T** split-screen mode, **Ymax** is calculated as **Ymin** + Δ**Y** * 50.

Cursor coordinates are displayed as eight-character numbers (which may include a negative sign, decimal point, and exponent) when **Float** mode is selected. **X** and **Y** are updated with a maximum accuracy of eight digits.

minimum and **maximum** on the **CALCULATE** menu are calculated with a tolerance of 1E-5; ∫**f(x)dx** is calculated at 1E-3. Therefore, the result displayed may not be accurate to all eight displayed digits. For most functions, at least five accurate digits exist. For **fMin(**, **fMax(**, and **fnInt(** on the **MATH** menu and **solve(** in the **CATALOG**, the tolerance can be specified.

Function Limits

Function	Range of Input Values
sin x, **cos** x, **tan** x	$0 \le |x| < 10^{12}$ (radian or degree)
sin^{-1} x, **cos**$^{-1}$ x	$-1 \le x \le 1$
ln x, **log** x	$10^{-100} < x < 10^{100}$
ex	$-10^{100} < x \le 230.25850929940$
10x	$-10^{100} < x < 100$
sinh x, **cosh** x	$|x| \le 230.25850929940$
tanh x	$|x| < 10^{100}$
sinh^{-1} x	$|x| < 5 \times 10^{99}$
cosh^{-1} x	$1 \le x < 5 \times 10^{99}$
tanh^{-1} x	$-1 < x < 1$
$\sqrt{x}$ (real mode)	$0 \le x < 10^{100}$
$\sqrt{x}$ (complex mode)	$|x| < 10^{100}$
$x!$	$-.5 \le x \le 69$, where x is a multiple of .5

Function Results

Function	Range of Result	
sin^{-1} x, **tan**$^{-1}$ x	$-90°$ to $90°$	or $-\pi / 2$ to $\pi / 2$ (radians)
cos^{-1} x	$0°$ to $180°$	or 0 to π (radians)

C

Appendix C:
Service and Warranty Information

Texas Instruments Support and Service

For general information

Home Page: education.ti.com

**KnowledgeBase and
e-mail inquiries:** education.ti.com/support

Phone: (800) TI-CARES / (800) 842-2737
For U.S., Canada, Mexico, Puerto Rico, and
Virgin Islands only

**International
information:** education.ti.com/international

For product (hardware) service

Customers in the U.S., Canada, Mexico, Puerto Rico and Virgin Islands: Always contact Texas Instruments Customer Support before returning a product for service.

All other customers: Refer to the leaflet enclosed with this product (hardware) or contact your local Texas Instruments retailer/distributor.

Texas Instruments (TI) Warranty Information

Customers in the U.S. and Canada Only

One-Year Limited Warranty for Commercial Electronic Product

This Texas Instruments ("TI") electronic product warranty extends only to the original purchaser and user of the product.

Warranty Duration. This TI electronic product is warranted to the original purchaser for a period of one (1) year from the original purchase date.

Warranty Coverage. This TI electronic product is warranted against defective materials and construction. **THIS WARRANTY IS VOID IF THE PRODUCT HAS BEEN DAMAGED BY ACCIDENT OR UNREASONABLE USE, NEGLECT, IMPROPER SERVICE, OR OTHER CAUSES NOT ARISING OUT OF DEFECTS IN MATERIALS OR CONSTRUCTION.**

Warranty Disclaimers. ANY IMPLIED WARRANTIES ARISING OUT OF THIS SALE, INCLUDING BUT NOT LIMITED TO THE IMPLIED WARRANTIES OF MERCHANTABILITY AND FITNESS FOR A PARTICULAR PURPOSE, ARE LIMITED IN DURATION TO THE ABOVE ONE-YEAR PERIOD. TEXAS INSTRUMENTS SHALL NOT BE LIABLE FOR LOSS OF USE OF THE PRODUCT OR OTHER INCIDENTAL OR CONSEQUENTIAL COSTS, EXPENSES, OR DAMAGES INCURRED BY THE CONSUMER OR ANY OTHER USER.

Some states/provinces do not allow the exclusion or limitation of implied warranties or consequential damages, so the above limitations or exclusions may not apply to you.

Legal Remedies. This warranty gives you specific legal rights, and you may also have other rights that vary from state to state or province to province.

Warranty Performance. During the above one (1) year warranty period, your defective product will be either repaired or replaced with a reconditioned model of an equivalent quality (at TI's option) when the product is returned, postage prepaid, to Texas Instruments Service Facility. The warranty of the repaired or replacement unit will continue for the warranty of the original unit or six (6) months, whichever is longer. Other than the postage requirement, no charge will be made for such repair and/or replacement. TI strongly recommends that you insure the product for value prior to mailing.

Software. Software is licensed, not sold. TI and its licensors do not warrant that the software will be free from errors or meet your specific requirements. **All software is provided "AS IS."**

Copyright. The software and any documentation supplied with this product are protected by copyright.

Australia & New Zealand Customers only

One-Year Limited Warranty for Commercial Electronic Product

This Texas Instruments electronic product warranty extends only to the original purchaser and user of the product.

Warranty Duration. This Texas Instruments electronic product is warranted to the original purchaser for a period of one (1) year from the original purchase date.

Warranty Coverage. This Texas Instruments electronic product is warranted against defective materials and construction. This warranty is void if the product has been damaged by accident or unreasonable use, neglect, improper service, or other causes not arising out of defects in materials or construction.

Warranty Disclaimers. Any implied warranties arising out of this sale, including but not limited to the implied warranties of merchantability and fitness for a particular purpose, are limited in duration to the above one-year period. Texas Instruments shall not be liable for loss of use of the product or other incidental or consequential costs, expenses, or damages incurred by the consumer or any other user.

Except as expressly provided in the One-Year Limited Warranty for this product, Texas Instruments does not promise that facilities for the repair of this product or parts for the repair of this product will be available.

Some jurisdictions do not allow the exclusion or limitation of implied warranties or consequential damages, so the above limitations or exclusions may not apply to you.

Legal Remedies. This warranty gives you specific legal rights, and you may also have other rights that vary from jurisdiction to jurisdiction.

Warranty Performance. During the above one (1) year warranty period, your defective product will be either repaired or replaced with a new or reconditioned model of an equivalent quality (at TI's option) when the product is returned to the original point of purchase. The repaired or replacement unit will continue for the warranty of the original unit or six (6) months, whichever is longer. Other than your cost to return the product, no charge will be made for such repair and/or replacement. TI strongly recommends that you insure the product for value if you mail it.

Software. Software is licensed, not sold. TI and its licensors do not warrant that the software will be free from errors or meet your specific requirements. **All software is provided "AS IS."**

Copyright. The software and any documentation supplied with this product are protected by copyright.

All Other Customers

For information about the length and terms of the warranty, refer to your package and/or to the warranty statement enclosed with this product, or contact your local Texas Instruments retailer/distributor.

Battery Information

When to Replace the Batteries

The TI-84 Plus uses five batteries: four AAA alkaline batteries and one SR44SW or 303 silver oxide backup battery. The silver oxide battery provides auxiliary power to retain memory while you replace the AAA batteries.

When the battery voltage level drops below a usable level, the TI-84 Plus:

Displays this message when you turn on the unit.

Displays this message when you attempt to download an application.

```
Your batteries
are low.

Recommend
change of
batteries.
```

```
Batteries
are low.
Change is
required.
```

Message A

Message B

After **Message A** is first displayed, you can expect the batteries to function for about one or two weeks, depending on usage. (This one-week to two-week period is based on tests with alkaline batteries; the performance of other types of batteries may vary.)

If **Message B** is displayed, you must replace the batteries immediately to successfully download an application.

Replace the silver oxide battery every three or four years.

Effects of Replacing the Batteries

Do not remove both types of batteries (AAA and silver oxide) at the same time. **Do not** allow the batteries to lose power completely. If you follow these guidelines and the steps for replacing batteries, you can replace either type of battery without losing any information in memory.

Battery Precautions

Take these precautions when replacing batteries.

• Do not leave batteries within reach of children

• Do not mix new and used batteries. Do not mix brands (or types within brands) of batteries.

• Do not mix rechargeable and nonrechargeable batteries.

• Install batteries according to polarity (+ and –) diagrams.

- Do not place nonrechargeable batteries in a battery recharger.

- Properly dispose of used batteries immediately. Do not leave them within the reach of children.

- Do not incinerate or dismantle batteries.

Replacing the Batteries

To replace the batteries, follow these steps.

1. Turn off the graphing calculator. Replace the slide cover over the keyboard to avoid inadvertently turning on the graphing calculator. Turn the back of the unit toward you.

2. Hold the graphing calculator upright, push downward on the latch on the top of the battery cover, and then pull the cover toward you.

    Note: To avoid loss of information stored in memory, you must turn off the graphing calculator. Do not remove the AAA batteries and the silver oxide battery simultaneously.

3. Replace all four AAA alkaline batteries simultaneously. Or, replace the silver oxide battery.

    - To replace the AAA alkaline batteries, remove all four discharged AAA batteries and install new ones according to the polarity (+ and –) diagram in the battery compartment.

    - To replace the silver oxide battery, remove the screw from the silver oxide battery cover, and then remove the cover. Install the new battery, + side up. Replace the cover and secure it with the screw. Use a SR44SW or 303 (or equivalent) silver oxide battery.

4. Replace the battery compartment cover. Turn the graphing calculator on and adjust the display contrast, if necessary, by pressing [2nd] [▲] or [▼].

In Case of Difficulty

Handling a Difficulty

To handle a difficulty, follow these steps.

1. If you cannot see anything on the screen, you may need to adjust the graphing calculator contrast.

   To darken the screen, press *and* release [2nd], and then press and hold [▲] until the display is sufficiently dark.

   To lighten the screen, press *and* release [2nd], and then press and hold [▼] until the display is sufficiently light.

2. If an error menu is displayed, follow these steps:

   • Note the error type (**ERR:***error type*).

   • Select **2:GOTO**, if it is available. The previous screen is displayed with the cursor at or near the error location.

   • Deteremine the error.

   • Correct the expression.

   Refer to the Error Conditions table for details about specific errors, if necessary.

3. If the busy indicator (dotted line) is displayed, a graph or program has been paused; the TI-84 Plus is waiting for input. Press [ENTER] to continue or press [ON] to break.

4. If a checkerboard cursor (▓) is displayed, then either you have entered the maximum number of characters in a prompt, or memory is full. If memory is full:

   • Press [2nd] [MEM] **2** to display the **MEMORY MANAGEMENT / DELETE** menu.

   • Select the type of data you want to delete, or select **1:All** for a list of all variables of all types. A screen is displayed listing each variable of the type you selected and the number of bytes each variable is using.

   • Press [▲] and [▼] to move the selection cursor (▶) next to the item you want to delete, and then press [DEL].

5. If the graphing calculator does not seem to work at all, be sure the alkaline batteries are fresh and that they are installed properly.

6. If the TI-84 Plus does not function even though you are sure that the batteries are fresh, you can try manually resetting it.

   • Remove all of the AAA batteries from the graphing calculator.

- Press and hold the ⟨ON⟩ key for ten seconds.
- Replace the batteries.
- Turn on the unit.

When you reset your graphing calculator, the contrast sometimes changes. If the screen is faded or blank, adjust the contrast by pressing ⟨2nd⟩ and releasing ⟨▲⟩ or ⟨▼⟩.

7. If the above solutions do not work you can reset all of the memory. The RAM, user data archive memory, and system variables are restored to factory settings when you reset all memory. All nonsystem variables, applications (Apps), and programs are deleted.

- Press ⟨2nd⟩ [MEM] to display the **MEMORY** menu.
- Select **7:Reset** to display the **RAM ARCHIVE ALL** menu.
- Press ⟨▶⟩⟨▶⟩ to display the **ALL** menu.
- Select **1:All Memory** to display the **RESET MEMORY** menu.
- To continue with the reset, select **2:Reset**. The message **Mem cleared** is displayed on the home screen.

Index

F

G

H

I